THE
AVENGERS
THE OFFICIAL QUIZ BOOK

Roy Bettridge

Published by
QUOIT MEDIA LIMITED
WWW.QUOITMEDIA.CO.UK

QUOIT

This edition first published in 2024 by Quoit Media Limited,
Brynmawr, Llanfair Caereinion, Powys, SY21 0DG

For more copies of this book, please email quoit@quoitmedia.co.uk

ISBN 978-1911-537-243

Cover design by Brett Jones. Edited and typeset by Duncan Lilly.

A CIP catalogue record for this book is available from the British Library.

Printed and bound in Great Britain by Clays Ltd, Elcograf S.p.A.

MIX
Paper | Supporting
responsible forestry
FSC® C018072
FSC
www.fsc.org

CONTENTS

IN MEMORIAM

This book is lovingly and respectfully dedicated to

Paul O'Grady
(1955 – 2023)

Comedian, Writer, Presenter and lifelong Avengers fan

IN MEMORIAM

This book is lovingly and respectfully dedicated to

Laurie Johnson
(1927 – 2024)

Television & Film composer, Band leader and Avengers alumni

IN MEMORIAM

This book is lovingly and respectfully dedicated to

Raymond Austin
(1932 – 2023)
Stunt man, Writer, Director and Avengers alumni

FOREWORD

I was the fourth Avenger woman, the fourth female aide to one of television's most charming heroes, John Steed, the man, the legend.

These were very big shoes to fill: before me strode Honor Blackman, Diana Rigg and Linda Thorson. By the time the role was mine it had been decided that John Steed would need yet another side-kick, a younger man to be the brawn behind the brains. We were Gambit and Purdey, although I was very nearly Charlie, as the original script intended. There was a popular scent called Charlie, there were *Charlie's Angels* about to burst onto the screens and I suggested Purdey, just the single name, after the gun manufacturer – which was kindly accepted by our three producers: Albert Fennell, Laurie Johnson, who wrote the theme music to this and many other shows, and Brian Clemens, who created the series.

To be given the part of the new girl was life-changing for me. As an actress who had never been to drama school or played in reps up and down the country, who had appeared in *Coronation Street* and a Dracula film, who

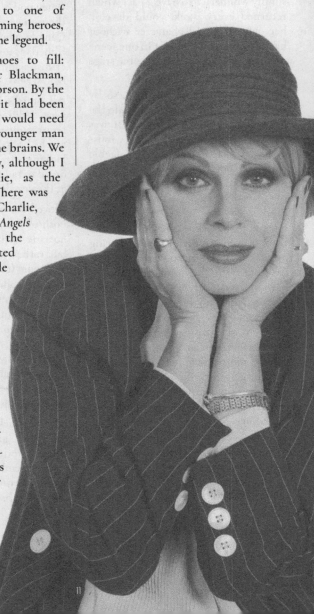

had played on stage in the West End, been countless girlfriends and secretaries but was always anxious to have a better crack of the whip; it was simply wonderful to have a part which returned every week, could develop her own style and character without having to make an impact in one scene only, the lot of all actors at some stage in their careers.

Everything was made on film, so by the end of two years we had made the equivalent of thirteen movies. It was the best training and the most excellent fun. Exhausting is a feeble word to describe how we all felt during the shooting: up first thing in the morning, straight to Pinewood Studios and into make-up, cram the lines for the scenes ahead into the front of your mind, do some limbering up if it was an action day (I loved working with the stuntmen: unsung heroes if ever there were), film all day with no time for lunch, as there was always an interview or costume fitting or a new skill to master. Once I was given quarter of an hour to learn to ride a motorbike, half an hour to become a proficient tap-dancer, which was obviously impossible and rather terrifying. I dangled from helicopters, ran along the ridges of roofs, went through a car wash on the top of an old jalopy, fought with cybernauts, sprinted along railway lines and emerged from the sea in a wet-suit in the freezing cold water off the coast of Scotland.

We attracted the finest actors in the land and I learnt so much watching them, and stealing from them their timing, their delivery, their camera-savvy awareness.

The New Avengers was filmed in Pinewood and then France; and when the money ran out there, we went to Canada where the last episodes were filmed, as autumn painted the forests crimson and the temperature dropped below zero.

All Steed's female companions were very different in looks and temperament, but we were all tough as old boots and perfectly capable of looking after ourselves and helping Steed to save the world every week, or, at the very least, right massive wrongs.

I loved the humour and the bish bash bosh of the stories. We never showed horrific killings, or nooses or blood; but rather like cowboy films, we got our man (or woman) by the end of each episode and usually had some cheerful banter before we strolled off into the sunset. There was a kind of youthful innocence about the series and now it would be hard to get it green-lit, as we say, as they would need more sex and violence and darker storylines before such a show would be commissioned.

So I was luckier than sunshine to get the part, and to have two years working on such a well-loved and long-remembered show. This fabulous book will nudge your own memories and bring back to life all that was so great about *The Avengers*.

Dame Joanna Lumley
October 2023

THE RULES

The Ministry of Fandom awaits your membership and The Avengers is the fantastic place to start.

Each question you face will score one point per question. Puzzles and Word Searches may score multiple points or bonus points. The special Sudoku offers a full quota of points per completed grid.

The total points on offer in each section will be listed, along with a place to enter your score - remember to be truthful and not a department traitor.

Your score will be placed into the chart at the end and will determine your ranking in the department.

The Ministry of Fandom strongly advises the viewing of "The Avengers" and a direct order from Mother states that the enjoyment of the show will enhance the quiz book experience and provide the answers you seek.

An important department directive is issued to you, the reader, in regard to Series 1; due to some of the episodes still being lost, the questions concerning narrative points have been helped along by the officially licensed Big Finish Productions audio adaptations, except where episodes or sequences of episodes survive intact.

RA-BOOM-DI-AY!!! HAPPY QUIZZING!!!

#1 - MRS EMMA PEEL

1 Mrs Emma Peel's husband was a missing what?

2 In the episode *The Forget Me Knot*; what is it that Emma advises Tara King on when they pass on the stairs to Steed's apartment?

3 What is Emma's maiden name?

4 Where was Peter Peel discovered to have been?

5 In which episode can Emma be found "in ladies' lingerie"?

6 What was the name of Emma's automation company?

7 Emma was the Queen of Sin in which episode?

8 What is the anagram of Emma in *The Winged Avenger*?

9 What colour is Emma's hair?

10 Who was the first casting choice for Mrs Emma Peel?

11 What is on Emma's front door in Series 4?

12 What car does Emma drive?

13 Apart from Steed, who is the best driver that Emma knows?

14 What present did Emma give to Steed that he wears?

15 Was Emma an amateur or a professional?

Points Available: **15**
Your current score: ____

#2 - CROSSWORD 1

Across

2 Emma Peel's mode of transport (5)

4 Diana Rigg became this in 1994 (4)

5 Episode title; *The _____ Avenger* (5)

7 The planet that was apparently invading; also the name of Miss Browne of the BVS (5)

8 This is highly improbable (7)

10 Episode title; Emma's end of a lifetime movie (4)

11 John Steed's trusted car (7)

Down

1 Town where Emma Peel was trapped by the villagers (12)

3 Steed and Emma found a room without one of these (4)

6 Call of an Avenger with wings (5)

9 Episode title; This was done to a deadly number (4)

Points Available: **11**

Anagram answer: _____ (1 extra point)

Your current score: _____

16

#3 - CONUNDRUM 1

This DJ was an Avenger from the beginning and always had a bowler hat in times of stress;

MC KANE TRACEPIE

Who is it?

_ _ _ _ _ _ _ _   _ _ _ _ _ _ _

Points Available: **1**
Your current score: ____

#4 - Under The Hat 1 - Department Trivia

1 Patrick Macnee's first name is Daniel – true or false?

2 Brian Clemens created *The Sweeney* – true or false?

3 Patrick Macnee was a nudist – true or false?

4 Paul O'Grady was NOT an Avengers fan – true or false?

5 *The Avengers* was sold to over 120 countries – true or false?

Points Available: **5**
Your current score: ____

#5 - Episodic Trivia - Series 1 - Part A

1 Hot Snow

1 What is the name of the killer who murders Peggy?

2 Did Dr Tredding say he would give the bride away or be the best man for Dr David Keel?

3 What is the weather like when Peggy is shot?

4 Who is the lady who telephones the surgery wanting to speak to David Keel?

5 What item are David Keel and Peggy looking at when she is gunned down?

2 Brought To Book

1 What is the name of the pub where John Steed finally introduces himself to David Keel?

2 Who is the gang member who has his face slashed with a cut throat razor?

3 What scheme is Steed trying to break up?

4 What are the names of the two gang leaders?

5 Where are drugs stashed as David Keel tries to infiltrate the gang, only to be interrupted by the law?

3 SQUARE ROOT OF EVIL

1 What was the nationality of the prisoner whom Steed took the place of while trying to investigate the forgery ring?

2 Who is Steed's superior?

3 What is the religious name given to one of the gang?

4 What was the name of the agent Steed replaced on the assignment?

5 What injury does Steed suffer in order to protect his cover?

4 NIGHTMARE

1 What is the name of the missing scientist?

2 What is the problem from which the Professor's wife, Faith, is suffering?

3 What does Keel hallucinate inside the lab?

4 Who is the medical informant for the villains?

5 What game does Steed play with Faith to put her nerves at ease?

5 CRESCENT MOON

1 What is the name of the kidnapped girl?

2 What is the name of the island Steed is visiting?

3 What is the main thing that Steed remarks about his police liaison, Carlos?

4 Who is the villainous retainer to the Mendoza family?

5 Who is the special patient David Keel is asked to treat?

6 GIRL ON THE TRAPEZE

1 What is the name muttered by the dying girl whom Dr Keel rescues from the Thames?

2 Where does the action take place?

3 After being roughed up backstage, what does David Keel offer Carol Wilson to calm her down?

4 What does David Keel tell the Superintendant not to take for his cold?

5 What is the name of the main clown?

6 What fake London code is given to the police officer?

7 Which member of the gang performed the jump from the bridge?

8 Where does the circus originate?

9 What kind of artist was Katrina Sandor?

10 What line is uttered by Carol Wilson when she and David Keel visit the circus and he believes that he has been recognised?

7 DIAMOND CUT DIAMOND

1 What is Steed's cover?

2 What crime is being committed?

3 What crime is Steed framed for?

4 What happens to make sure that Steed falls in line with the criminals?

5 Who is the unfortunate victim whom Steed has apparently killed?

8 THE RADIOACTIVE MAN

1 What is the name of the man everyone ends up chasing?

2 What is happening concurrently with Dr Graham as he assists David Keel?

3 What is being carried around to cause the sickness?

4 What is the name of the little boy?

5 What device is used to help find the radioactive man?

9 ASHES OF ROSES

1 Who owns the hairdressing salon?

2 What main crimes are being committed?

3 What item in the salon nearly deals with Carol Wilson permanently?

4 Which criminal does Steed recognise?

5 What favour does Steed ask of David Keel at the end?

10 HUNT THE MAN DOWN

1 Who is the man released from prison?

2 Who are the two thugs?

3 How much is the loot that Steed wants recovered?

4 Who is kidnapped to force Keel's co-operation in finding the money?

5 Where is the money hidden?

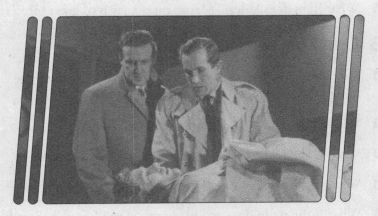

11 PLEASE, DON'T FEED THE ANIMALS

1 What animal retrieves the packages in the zoo?

2 What army rank is Renton-Stephens?

3 What kind of pit does the first agent fall into?

4 Who is Steed keeping an eye on?

5 What kind of brawl involves Steed and Keel at the club?

12 DANCE WITH DEATH

1 What is the name of the lady who comes to David Keel for help?

2 What item of David Keel's is used to commit murder?

3 What does Steed notice about the surgery when he visits?

4 What catalogue does Steed mention when he notices someone at the dance studio?

5 What item does Valerie Marne carry that is of great interest?

13 ONE FOR THE MORTUARY

1 How does Steed send the microfilm to David Keel for the trip to Geneva?

2 Where does David Keel meet with Steed?

3 What is the recognisable feature of the killer, Benson?

4 What is the profession of Bernard Bourg?

5 What is the main instruction given to David Keel by Steed before he leaves for Geneva?

Points Available: **70**
Your current score: _____

#6 - QUICK TEST - SERIES 1

1 What was the title of the first ever episode of *The Avengers*?

    A) Hot Snow   *B) Hot Sun*   *C) Hot Rain*

2 Which episode introduced Carol Wilson?

    A) Brought   *B) Brought*   *C) Brought*
     To Pen   *To Book*   *To Paper*

3 Which episode introduced One-Ten?

    A) Ruby Cut   *B) Diamond Cut*   *C) Diamond Cut*
      Ruby   *Diamond*   *Glass*

Points Available: 3
Your current score: ____

#7 - Drink, Mrs Peel??

C	H	A	M	P	O	I	C	A	W	G	T	Y	U	B
T	E	D	O	C	H	A	M	P	A	G	N	E	N	Y
S	J	P	A	X	T	E	R	J	A	E	B	A	S	R
A	B	A	S	V	Z	T	N	A	H	K	L	X	E	F
V	S	T	E	A	V	Q	Y	B	M	X	G	N	G	H
E	F	A	C	O	C	H	A	M	P	A	G	N	E	A
N	N	R	A	A	X	H	Y	O	Z	A	P	Q	E	Z
C	A	A	T	N	O	T	A	E	P	E	A	J	V	X
H	A	P	H	Q	R	W	A	M	B	H	X	V	N	Q
A	C	D	Y	A	N	K	A	M	P	L	I	E	P	U
M	B	C	Y	M	J	H	X	A	C	A	C	B	U	I
P	V	M	W	M	C	T	G	H	X	L	G	P	R	Y
A	Z	H	H	E	D	A	H	B	A	E	Y	N	D	T
G	B	C	Y	E	S	E	C	Z	A	V	T	Q	E	O
N	N	H	Q	X	A	V	E	B	S	T	K	L	Y	E
E	D	B	A	K	V	A	L	O	H	C	M	V	N	F
D	E	T	S	B	N	E	N	G	A	P	M	A	H	C

How many times can you find the drink
that features regularly in *The Avengers*?

BONUS ALERT: Find Steed's partners
for 1 extra point per partner.

Points Available: **7**
Your current score: ____

#8 - Conundrum 2

Shakespeare-trained and after completing their Avenging, this person became a DBE;

IDA G RAGNI

Who is it?

_ _ _ _ _ _   _ _ _ _

#9 - Under The Hat 2 - Department Trivia

1 Patrick Macnee made a cameo in the 1998 *The Avengers* movie – true or false?

2 Patrick Macnee's father was a racehorse trainer nicknamed Shrimp – true or false?

3 Four stars from *The Avengers* and *The New Avengers* have appeared in James Bond movies – true or false?

4 The man behind *Doctor Who* was also part of the creative team behind *The Avengers* – true or false?

5 Ray Austin started on *The Avengers* as a stunt man – true or false?

6 There were several multi-arc stories and two-parters across *The Avengers* series – true or false?

Points Available: **6**
Your current score: ____

#10 - Episodic Trivia - Series 1 - Part B

14 The Springers

1 Where is the principal setting for the episode?

2 What is the name of the criminal Keel is impersonating?

3 Where are the prisoners taken after they manage to escape?

4 What is the name of the female agent assigned to help Steed?

5 What is Steed's cover when visiting the school?

15 The Frighteners

1 What is the name of the liquid Dr Keel uses to threaten the villain known as The Deacon?

2 What is the name of the beater who ends up with a neck issue?

3 What was the name of the taxi driver at Steed's disposal?

4 What kind of contract is being issued to a customer?

5 What does Keel tell Sir Thomas Weller to keep an eye on?

6 What nationality is Beppe?

7 What is the name of the Inspector who liaises with Steed?

8 What is the name of the lady claiming to be De Willoughby's mother?

9 What does Steed offer to give Moxon whilst wielding his razor?

10 How does De Willoughby leave David Keel's surgery?

16 THE YELLOW NEEDLE

1 What is the condition of Sir Wilberforce Lungi that is being treated by Dr David Keel?

2 Who does Steed pose as when he visits Tenebra?

3 What is the name of the society that is trying to kill Sir Wilberforce?

4 What did Sir Wilberforce practice before going into politics?

5 Who is the highest suspect on Steed's list?

17 DEATH ON THE SLIPWAY

1 Where is the main setting for the episode?

2 What is the name of the enemy agent who recognises Steed and tries to kill him?

3 What is Steed's cover?

4 What is the name of the worker who is being blackmailed?

5 What device does Steed have to find and deal with?

18 DOUBLE DANGER

1 Who organises Ted Mace's escape from prison?

2 What items are at the heart of all the double crosses?

3 What address is Dr. Keel given when visited by Lola at the surgery?

4 Out of Lowestein and Bruton – who is one of the villains?

5 What is the name of the person who holds the plot?

19 TOY TRAP

1 What is the name of the girl placed into the care of Dr David Keel as he helps Steed?

2 What is the racket that Steed is trying to break apart?

3 What is the name of the department store?

4 Where does Steed hide as he entraps the criminals?

5 Who turns out to be the vice ring leader?

20 TUNNEL OF FEAR

1 Who is the criminal who stumbles into Dr Keel's surgery with a shoulder wound and claiming he's been framed for a crime he didn't commit?

2 What is the occupation of Jack Wickram?

3 What does Steed bring to Dr Keel's surgery?

4 What car is Steed driving that gets stolen?

5 What is Steed's cover?

6 What is the apparent bluff used by Steed against Jack Wickram and his men?

7 What is David Keel's golfing handicap; revealed by Steed while under hypnosis?

8 How did David Keel help Harry Black regain his memory?

9 What is Steed's code-name when he telephones One-Ten?

10 What is the location of the funfair?

21 THE FAR DISTANT DEAD

1 What disaster caused Dr David Keel and Dr Ampara Sandoval to be united to help a relief effort?

2 Where is the location of events?

3 What is the deadly chemical that is being misinterpreted as cooking oil?

4 Who is the mastermind behind the fatalities?

5 What is the name of the man sent to find and kill Keel?

22 KILL THE KING

1 Where does the first attempt to kill King Tenuphon take place?

2 Who is the man who arrives at the residence of Zoe Carter?

3 Who is the foreign office official whom Steed deals with?

4 How is the King to be distracted and drawn into the killer's sights?

5 Who is the main enemy of the King?

23 DEAD OF WINTER

1 What is the name of the war criminal frozen and brought back to life?

2 What is the name of the female agent who meets with Steed?

3 What is the name of the group David Keel is to infiltrate?

4 Who amongst the workers does Steed rub up the wrong way?

5 Who was Dr Kreutzer's first experiment?

24 THE DEADLY AIR

1 What is the name of the laboratory?

2 What is being tested?

3 What animal do Dr David Keel and Steed perform a test on?

4 What is the name of the eccentric scientist whom Keel visits?

5 Who is the villain revealed to be?

25 A CHANGE OF BAIT

1 What is the cargo that is being used against Archie Duncan?

2 What is Archie Duncan's relationship to Carol Wilson?

3 What medical matter brings Archie to David Keel?

4 Where do Steed and David Keel become trapped?

5 What is the name of the unscrupulous insurer?

26 DRAGONSFIELD

1 What is being tested at the centre?

2 Which boss is Steed reporting to?

3 Who is the assistant to Dr Reddington?

4 Who is the security officer at the centre?

5 Who is revealed to be the villain?

Points Available: 75
Your current score: _____

#11 - BEHIND THE SCENES - SERIES 1

1 What is the name of the series that preceded *The Avengers*, starring Ian Hendry as Dr Geoffrey Brent?

A) Police
Officer

B) Police
Commissioner

C) Police
Surgeon

2 Name the composer of *The Avengers* theme from Series 1 to 3

A) John
Bonham

B) John
Dankworth

C) John
McVie

3 What was Brian Clemens' first story written for *The Avengers*?

A) Hot
Snow

B) Brought
To Book

C) One For
The Mortuary

4 In what year did Ian Hendry become the recipient of *This is Your Life*; being surprised Avengers style by host Eamonn Andrews and Patrick Macnee?

A) 1964

B) 1974

C) 1984

5 Who was the first producer of *The Avengers*?

A) Leonard
White

B) Leonard
Black

C) Leonard
Green

6 Who directed the first episode of *The Avengers*?

A) Don Leaver

B) Don Sharp

C) Don Black

7 Who was the famous dog trainer who worked on Series 1?

    A) Barbara   B) Barbara   C) Barbara
    Windsor   Gordon   Wodehouse

8 What was Dennis Spooner's first episode for the series?

    A) Please,   B) Please, Don't   C) Please,
    Don't Look   Feed The Animals   Help Me

9 Who started out as a production designer in Series 1 and went on to become a director on the series; directing '*Game*', '*They Keep Killing Steed*' and '*Tale of the Big Why*'?

    A) Robert Asher   B) Robert Day   C) Robert Fuest

Points Available: **9**
Your current score: _____

#12 – Dr David Keel

1 What two letters are associated with Keel's profession?

2 David Keel used a syringe filled with Witch-hazel as a weapon in which episode?

3 What organisation invited David Keel to Geneva in '*One For The Mortuary*'?

4 Who was David Keel's partner in his practice?

5 What is David Keel on the verge of when we first meet him?

6 What was the name of David Keel's fiancée?

7 In which episode do David Keel and John Steed physically come to blows?

8 What is David Keel's drink of choice?

9 In '*Toy Trap*', what was David Keel's past connection to Bunty Seaton?

10 Who comes to his old friend, David Keel, for his medical check-up in '*The Yellow Needle*'?

Points Available: **10**
Your current score: _____

#13 - Have A Word!

E	N	D	O	P	T	L	A	K	C	O	L	R	A	W
R	O	L	E	V	J	S	B	R	O	T	L	K	X	D
R	H	E	A	H	J	B	D	K	O	C	M	A	V	E
A	J	I	G	I	K	I	L	D	A	D	E	M	P	A
Z	K	F	S	H	N	P	K	P	D	M	N	B	C	Z
I	R	S	P	L	I	T	P	E	C	Q	B	A	L	X
B	C	N	A	B	A	C	E	G	W	P	C	I	P	E
B	N	O	F	A	V	T	Q	R	V	Y	M	A	B	R
U	X	G	N	A	S	B	Y	O	C	X	P	G	H	A
L	Q	A	K	C	V	G	E	K	A	R	D	N	A	M
L	K	R	N	S	E	G	W	D	K	P	I	L	R	T
S	L	D	X	C	B	R	A	D	M	W	J	M	K	H
E	P	A	D	H	A	M	T	H	A	E	V	S	E	G
Y	H	M	G	H	I	K	D	O	A	H	J	S	N	I
E	T	H	I	N	G	U	M	A	J	I	G	B	A	N

Find the following episode titles:

NIGHTMARE	INTERCRIME	SPLIT
WARLOCK	CONCERTO	PANDORA
DRAGONSFIELD	MANDRAKE	THINGUMAJIG
BULLSEYE	EPIC	BIZARRE

BONUS ALERT: Find the bowler hatted hero for an extra point.

Points Available: **13**
Your current score: _____

#14 - UNDER THE HAT 3 - SERIES 1

1 Ray Austin wrote the first ever episode of *The Avengers* – true or false?

2 Ian Hendry was never married – true or false?

3 John Dankworth was a jazz musician – true or false?

4 Patrick Macnee appeared in every episode of *The Avengers* – true or false?

5 Patrick Macnee's second wife appeared in *The Avengers* – true or false?

Points Available: **5**
Your current score: _____

#15 - CROSSWORD 2

Across

1 Remote Electromatic Agent Killer (5)

4 First name of Tara King actress (5)

6 Episode titles; *To Your Leader* and *Over* (4)

7 Episode title; loss of memory (6)

8 Place of affection where Steed hides the falcon dagger in *Legacy of Death* (4)

9 Name of Mother's assistant (6)

Down

2 Episode title; featured Lady Diana Forbes-Blakeney (6)

3 Episode title; Tara King is drugged to play this person (7)

5 Episode title; *Love ...* (3)

6 Surname of Tara King actress (7)

7 Lady in charge of department in Mother's absence (6)

Points Available: **10**
Anagram answer: _____ (1 extra point)
Your current score: ____

#16 - EPISODIC TRIVIA - SERIES 2 - PART A

1 DEAD ON COURSE

1 What was the name of the villain who tried to make a getaway with the ill-gotten gains of the plane crashes?

2 In which country does the action take place?

3 How did Martin King deal with the gun-wielding Mother Superior at the convent?

4 How did Steed discover the next plane being targeted?

5 What made the pilot the odd one out from all of the other crash victims?

2 MISSION TO MONTREAL

1 What was the name of the actress under Martin King's care?

2 What is the name given to the document being smuggled?

3 Where does the action take place?

4 What was Steed's cover?

5 Who is the double agent working with Steed?

3 THE SELL OUT

1 Who is Steed's superior, who has assigned him to look after Etienne Roland?

2 What is the cover of Frazer, the man tailing Steed?

3 Who was the traitor?

4 Where does Steed meet One-Twelve?

5 How does Dr King take down a gunman aiming for Steed?

4 DEATH DISPATCH

1 What is the location for Steed's assignment as a courier for important government dispatches with Cathy as his cover?

2 Who was the president who was trying to start a coup until Steed and Cathy Gale got involved?

3 What is Juanita?

4 What does Steed greet Cathy Gale with on her arrival?

5 How did Steed and Cathy get the upper hand over the president?

5 WARLOCK

1 Where does Steed find Cathy Gale working when he needs to inquire about the hex sent to Peter Neville?

2 What was the name of the villain?

3 What time did Cathy Gale say she was born?

4 What kind of magic is explored?

5 Who is the housekeeper to scientist Peter Neville?

6 PROPELLANT 23

1 What is the name of the agent Steed is to meet?

2 What is the nickname of the balding officer in the airport?

3 What is the fuel called by Steed's superiors over the phone?

4 Who takes the fuel, believing it to be alcohol?

5 Where did Cathy Gale secrete her gun?

7 MR TEDDY BEAR

1 What is the poison used to murder Colonel Wayne-Gilley?

2 What is the asking price for Mr Teddy Bear?

3 With what did Mr Teddy Bear attempt to kill Steed?

4 What animal prints were found on the cigarette case?

5 What gems did Mr Teddy Bear wish Cathy Gale to pay him for killing Steed?

8 THE DECAPOD

1 Who was revealed to be the masked wrestler?

2 What sport is the favourite of President Yakob Borb?

3 Where does the final fight occur?

4 At which embassy does Yakob Borb reside?

5 What is the name of the real Decapod?

9 BULLSEYE

1 What is the name of the business that Henry Cade is unsuccessfully trying to take over?

2 When meeting Henry Cade; how did he describe his taste to Cathy Gale?

3 Who was the final director who was approached by Cade?

4 Who was Mrs Reynolds' lover?

5 What did Steed act as for Cathy during the assignment?

10 THE REMOVAL MEN

1 Where did Steed hide the political film star Nicole Cauvin?

2 What did Steed initially steal from Jack Dragna?

3 What happened to the fence, Benaggio?

4 What song does Venus play at the piano?

5 What is the name of the club owned by Jack Dragna?

11 THE MAURITIUS PENNY

1 What happened to Goodchild at the auction?

2 Where did Steed visit as Goodchild, only to find that his cover was rumbled?

3 What does Cathy accidentally bid for at the auction?

4 What did Steed recognise about the fake policemen in his flat?

5 What is the name of Steed's cleaner?

12 Death Of A Great Dane

1 What was the name of the villain in charge of the organisation?

2 What is discovered in the pet cemetery rather than a dead animal?

3 In what part of the body were the diamonds smuggled?

4 What is the name of the deceased millionaire being kept apparently alive?

5 How many Great Dane dogs were there?

13 Death On The Rocks

1 What containers were the diamonds being smuggled in?

2 In which area of London were the illicit stones being traded?

3 What cover does Steed insist upon for himself and Cathy?

4 Who is the murderous beautician?

5 Who turned out to be the head of the smuggling ring?

Points Available: **65**
Your current score: ____

#17 - Quick Test - Series 2

1 Name the episode where Steed applies suntan oil to One Ten's back

    A) The Painting Men   *B) The Removal Men*   *C) The Decorating Men*

2 Who is the assassin Olaf Pomeroy?

    A) Mr Teddy Bear   *B) Mr Penny Lane*   *C) Mr Sugar Daddy*

3 What is the name of the liquid Steed has to collect from the dead agent Meyer that is code-named as fruit juice?

    A) Propellant 23   *B) The Titanic*   *C) Area 52*

4 Which episode involves the search for an unbreakable cup?

    A) Immortal Tea   *B) Immortal Coffee*   *C) Immortal Clay*

5 The villain of a Venus Smith episode – but what in reality is a decapod?

    A) A Crustacean   *B) A Jellyfish*   *C) A Manta Ray*

Points Available: **5**
Your current score: ____

#18 - UNDER THE HAT 4 - SERIES 2

1 Patrick Macnee used to make up his dialogue – true or false?

2 Cyd Child was stunt double for Honor Blackman – true or false?

3 John Dankworth was married to jazz singer Cleo Laine – true or false?

4 Kenny Ball and his Jazzmen were set to back Venus Smith in a Series 2 episode – true or false?

5 Honor Blackman was the first choice to play Cathy Gale – true or false?

Points Available: **5**

Your current score: ____

#19 - Episodic Trivia - Series 2 - Part B

14 Traitor In Zebra

1 What drink does Steed order from the bar?

2 How was Lieutenant Graham killed?

3 How did Rankin pass on messages to Linda in the shop?

4 How were messages passed on via the pub?

5 How does Steed deal with Joe Franks?

15 The Big Thinker

1 What was the name of the super computer?

2 What is Dr Kearns' biggest bad habit?

3 How was Dr Clemens killed?

4 What arcade game was Steed playing as he discussed the situation with Cathy Gale?

5 What code-name did Steed use when telephoning the police to come and take Brewster away after he and his accomplice broke into Cathy's flat?

16 INTERCRIME

1 Who was the assassin that Steed asked Cathy to impersonate?

2 Who runs the London office of Intercrime?

3 What is Cathy asked to act as for the suspected traitor?

4 Who helps Hilda Stern in her escape plans?

5 Who is the latest target of Intercrime?

17 IMMORTAL CLAY

1 What unbreakable item did Allan Marling claim to have created?

2 Where does One-Ten brief Steed?

3 What is the name of De Groot's bodyguard who lays Steed out in the pottery?

4 What item is used to blackmail Allan Marling into co-operating?

5 Where is Landers' body found by Cathy and Richard Marling?

18 BOX OF TRICKS

1 What did Dr Gallam claim to be?

2 What phrase did Venus claim to hear, both in the club and when visiting Kathleen Sutherland's house?

3 What cover did Steed have in the Sutherland house?

4 What device was hidden in the packages placed in General Sutherland's wheelchair?

5 What member of the club was working with Dr Gallam?

19 THE GOLDEN EGGS

1 What was the name of the magazine that Cathy Gale claimed to be writing for in her visit to Dr Ashe?

2 What is the obsession of villain Julius Redfern?

3 What morning activity is Steed doing when discussing the death of DeLeon?

4 Where is Steed staying while Cathy Gale stays at his flat?

5 What is the current strain of virus that is present in the eggs and dubbed by Dr Ashe as the world's most recent killer?

20 SCHOOL FOR TRAITORS

1 Which of Steed's superiors gives him his instructions?

2 Who was the student Steed enlists to help find information?

3 Who orders Ted East to kill Steed?

4 Who was Steed researching as part of his cover?

5 What is the profession of Claire Summers?

21 THE WHITE DWARF

1 What name was shared by the brothers involved with the Ministry of Science and the Stock Market, respectively?

2 What is the name of the observatory?

3 What direction does Cathy Gale confirm the white dwarf would be heading along, while taking the Earth with it?

4 Which of Steed's dogs is in this episode?

5 Who reveals that they murdered Professor Richter and Professor Rahim?

22 MAN IN THE MIRROR

1 How did Venus Smith accidentally find the supposedly dead agent Victor Trevellyan?

2 What is the name of the person who stole Venus's camera and works in the cafe?

3 How long does One-Six give Steed to wrap up the case?

4 Who is the man helping Trevellyan?

5 Where does Steed leave Venus while he looks around the funfair?

23 CONSPIRACY OF SILENCE

1 What phrase is announced to Carlo by to remind him of his oath to the mafia?

2 In what three locations does Steed tell Cathy Gale there has been a recent crackdown operation on dope peddling on the continent?

3 What activity is Steed doing when he is shot at?

4 Who is the clown that Carlo takes the place of so he can hide in plain sight?

5 What is the name of the agent keeping an eye on Carlo to make sure that he kills Steed?

24 A CHORUS OF FROGS

1 What is the name of the group that loses its agents Stephanopoulous and Jackson?

2 Where does the action take place?

3 What is the name of the man that One-Six sends Steed to keep an eye on?

4 To how many fathoms was Stephanopoulous said to have dived?

5 Where did Steed stow away?

25 Six Hands Across A Table

1 What is the name of Cathy Gale's potential love interest?

2 How does Steed get into Cathy's room at the Waldner residence?

3 What is the name of Cathy's friend and Oliver Waldner's daughter?

4 How many times is Brian Collier attacked?

5 Who from within the Reniston group grew a conscience about the murder of Herbert Collier and the attacks on Brian Collier, leading him to make a statement to the police?

26 Killer Whale

1 What is the substance being smuggled into the boxing gym?

2 What is the name of the designer helping to make the illegal scent?

3 How long has Steed staked out the gym?

4 Cathy is the manager of which young boxer?

5 Which of the boxers turns up dead?

#20 - Quick Test - Series 2 - Part 2

1 What is the name of Steed's would-be assassin in 'Conspiracy of Silence'?

    A) The Professor   B) Carlo   C) Sica

2 What was the Christian name of Dr King?

    A) Martin   B) Marvin   C) Melvin

3 Venus Smith was what by profession?

    A) Doctor   B) Singer   C) Builder

4 How does Steed get Joe Franks to disarm his bomb in 'Traitor in Zebra'?

    A) Traps him with it   B) Asks politely   C) Disarms it himself

5 What kind of magic were Steed and Cathy investigating in 'Warlock'?

    A) Black Magic   B) White Magic   C) Every Little Thing She Does is Magic

Points Available: **5**

Your current score: _____

1 Douglas Muir played One-Ten in *The Avengers* but who did his daughter Gillian play in series 2?

    A) Judy   *B) Julie*   *C) Punch*

2 What black material was famously worn by Honor Blackman in the series?

    A) Suede   *B) Silk*   *C) Leather*

3 James Mitchell wrote the episodes 'Man With Two Shadows' and 'Immortal Clay' for *The Avengers*. But what is the series that he is famous for creating?

    A) Callan   *B) Fallon*   *C) Dave Allen*

4 Which designer who later became a series director designed only one episode for series 2?

    A) Robert Roost   *B) Robert Fuest*   *C) Robert Juiced*

5 Which early series director set a certain style of film-making within the episodes he directed?

    A) Peter Hammond   *B) Peter Gammond*   *C) Peter Lambond*

Points Available: 5
Your current score: ____

This person was an Avenger before landing in gold and tangling with 007

CARLA H MONOKOB

Who is it?

_ _ _ _ _ _ _ _ _ _ _ _ _

#23 - Partners

Y	F	C	A	T	H	E	R	I	N	E	G	A	L	E
E	A	B	F	H	K	A	J	L	E	N	M	B	V	G
D	D	A	S	B	J	T	E	Y	T	W	H	A	S	G
R	A	T	U	A	R	H	E	Q	B	C	A	J	W	N
U	S	Q	D	F	G	H	I	L	A	G	E	R	Y	I
P	H	A	W	M	V	N	M	E	R	T	O	P	E	K
W	T	S	D	A	V	I	D	K	E	E	L	J	N	A
A	I	C	M	R	K	L	S	D	M	F	C	Z	A	R
X	M	E	Q	T	G	H	J	E	M	K	S	Q	J	A
C	S	A	T	I	V	R	I	S	A	H	N	V	I	T
A	S	C	H	N	Q	T	P	A	P	U	S	E	L	D
V	U	B	A	K	W	Y	O	P	E	T	A	R	O	H
B	N	D	G	I	E	U	L	U	E	B	C	B	K	Y
N	E	V	W	N	Q	A	U	I	L	K	T	R	J	F
K	V	S	Y	G	T	I	B	M	A	G	E	K	I	M

Find Steed's partners in crime solving

DAVID KEEL	MARTIN KING
CATHERINE GALE	VENUS SMITH
EMMA PEEL	MIKE GAMBIT
TARA KING	PURDEY

Points Available: **8**

Your current score: _____

#24 - Episodic Trivia - Series 3 - Part A

1 CONCERTO

1 What is the name of the pianist?

2 What kind of establishment is used in a blackmail plot?

3 What game is Cathy Gale subjected to as she is tied to a chair?

4 What is the name of the agent assigned to look after the pianist?

5 What VIP will be attending the piano recital and is the target of assassination?

2 BRIEF FOR MURDER

1 Who is the person Steed wants to murder?

2 What are the names of the crooked lawyer brothers?

3 What did Cathy Gale ask the brothers for help in committing?

4 What item of Steed's apparel was found at the scene of the crime but was found in court to be too large to fit?

5 Where was Cathy Gale killed?

3 THE NUTSHELL

1 On what level do the civil servants get off?

2 What biscuits does Steed offer to Cathy Gale?

3 What is Steed talking in when he receives the phone call?

4 How many volts of electricity shock Steed when he is detained by Venner?

5 Who was the double agent who alerted Steed that Big Ben was going to be stolen?

4 THE GOLDEN FLEECE

1 Where does Steed pick up the wrong coat?

2 What was the name of the criminal whom Steed was attempting to catch?

3 In what location is the army camp where Cathy takes a job?

4 How did Steed discover the Yan Sing restaurant?

5 How much was on the cheque found in the pocket of the coat that Steed took accidentally?

5 DEATH A LA CARTE

1 What was Steed's alias?

2 What food item is used to try to kill Emir Abdulla Akabar?

3 What is the name of the Emir's doctor?

4 What is the name of the nervous kitchen runner?

5 What nationality is Umberto pretending to be?

6 MAN WITH TWO SHADOWS

1 Where does Steed claim to have killed his double?

2 What was the name of the holiday camp?

3 What three personalities were given to brainwashed agent Peter Barowski?

4 What do Charles and Cathy Gale enjoy as they listen to a tape recording of Barowski?

5 According to Charles, how many days did the enemy hold Steed for?

7 DON'T LOOK BEHIND YOU

1 What was the name of Cathy Gale's article?

2 Where was Cathy Gale staying for the weekend?

3 What kind of car was Steed driving?

4 What was the name of the young man claiming to be a film director?

5 What was the name of Cathy Gale's tormentor?

8 THE GRANDEUR THAT WAS ROME

1 Sir Bruno Lucer worked for which organisation?

2 What people from history are being celebrated?

3 What part of Steed's umbrella was brought out for a fight?

4 What language do Steed and Cathy Gale speak at the end?

5 Who did Sir Bruno try to emulate?

9 THE UNDERTAKERS

1 What is Cathy cleaning when Steed arrives at her apartment?

2 What was the name of the scientist whom Steed had to accompany to New York?

3 What did Cathy Gale do with the jellied bumble bees?

4 What does Cathy Gale discover about the residents of Adelphi Park?

5 What does Steed do to the statue after the gun battle?

10 DEATH OF A BATMAN

1 What was the crime being committed by Teale and Van Doren?

2 What is the name of Steed's dog?

3 Towards the end of which war did Steed have a Batman?

4 What sport is Steed currently hung up on?

5 How much was Steed left in the will?

11 BUILD A BETTER MOUSETRAP

1 What are the names of the daughters who have taken possession of their late father's jamming device?

2 Where are the sisters living?

3 Which member of the biker gang is suspicious of Cathy Gale's intentions?

4 What device of Cynthia's gets destroyed?

5 Who is after the jamming device?

12 NOVEMBER FIVE

1 What was stolen from a truck en route to an RAF base in East Anglia?

2 How long did it take for the ambulance to reach Michael Dyter after he was shot?

3 What sector did Mark St John work in?

4 When does Dyter time his operation for?

5 How much was the blackmail amount in the ransom?

13 SECOND SIGHT

1 What is the location of the clinic?

2 Where is the pathway laid out to help Marten Halverson?

3 What item is being smuggled?

4 What is the name of the female friend supposedly helping Marten Halverson?

5 What is the name of the fussy doctor who insists on overseeing the operation?

Points Available: **65**
Your current score: _____

#25 – BEHIND THE SCENES – SERIES 3

1 What is the name of the script editor who went on to become the producer of *The Avengers* in Series 3?

    A) John Bryce   *B) John Rice*   *C) John Steed*

2 What is the name of the script editor who had a family connection to the popular book *The Darling Buds of May*?

    A) Richard Mates   *B) Richard Bates*   *C) Richard Dates*

3 What was the name of Brian Clemens' real-life friend that was used for one of the central characters in the episode 'Brief for Murder'?

    A) Ronnie Barker   *B) Ronnie Corbett*   *C) Ronnie Wescott*

4 Who is behind the pseudonym Richard Lucas?

    A) Terrance Dicks   *B) Brian Clemens*   *C) Mills*
    & Malcolm Hulke   *& Richard Bates*   *& Boon*

5 How long was wrestler Jackie Pallo unconscious after the fight with Honor Blackman in '*Mandrake*'?

    A) 2 Minutes   *B) 6 Minutes*   *C) 7½ Minutes*

6 What novelty song was recorded by Patrick Macnee and Honor Blackman that failed to ignite the charts in 1964 but became a top 5 hit in 1990?

    A) Twirling Umbrellas   *B) Kinky Boots*   *C) Jaunty Hats*

#26 – EPISODIC TRIVIA – SERIES 3 – PART B

14 THE SECRETS BROKER

1 Where is the microdot that alerts Steed to the wine shop?

2 How long has Steed been awake when he arrives at Cathy Gale's flat?

3 What is the name of the scientist who flippantly refers to Steed as 'the man from the Ministry'?

4 What is the name of the wine shop?

5 Who is the elderly blackmailer?

15 THE GILDED CAGE

1 What is the commodity that Steed and Cathy Gale use to trap J.P. Spagge?

2 What does Steed admire about J.P. Spagge's butler, Fleming?

3 What is the name of the Inspector working with Steed to catch the gang?

4 Who leads the gang of robbers?

5 What percentage is the reward for the recovered loot?

16 THE MEDICINE MEN

1 What was the country described as being the size of a postage stamp?

2 What is the brand name for the Willis-Sopwith Pharmaceutical product that is being targeted by imitators?

3 What does Steed hate doing in a hurry?

4 How did Miss Tu Schu Yung die?

5 What word do Steed and Cathy place onto the Willis-Sopwith fake labels in a night-time visit to the printers?

17 THE WHITE ELEPHANT

1 On what day of history was the recording of 'The White Elephant' made?

2 What substance is being smuggled?

3 What kind of animal is Noah Marshall's pet, Samba?

4 Where does Cathy Gale end up trapped?

5 What is the name of the gun manufacturers?

18 DRESSED TO KILL

1 Where did Cathy Gale go on holiday?

2 Where was the fancy dress party held?

3 From what location did the train start?

4 What was the name of the mouthy Robin Hood?

5 There was a Pussy Cat, a Sheriff, a Policeman, a Highwaywoman, a Cowboy... Who is missing?

6 Who was the first victim of the special passengers?

19 THE WRINGER

1 What is the name of the agent who has been missing for six weeks?

2 What item did Steed keep an eye on to contain the effects of his conditioning?

3 What in the 'official handbook' is Cathy Gale teased about by Steed when she sums up his predicament?

4 Charles sees it as a privilege to do what?

5 Where is the interrogation unit?

20 THE LITTLE WONDERS

1 What was the name of the organisation that used the church as its cover?

2 What list is given over by Steed and developed by Dr Beardmore and Sister Johnson?

3 Where did Steed say he was the vicar of?

4 How many gunmen are with Steed?

5 What sweets does Steed take from the tuck shop?

21 MANDRAKE

1 What was the poison that was being used by Roy Hopkins and Dr Macombie to kill their victims?

2 What church held the victims?

3 Whose death put Steed onto what was happening in Cornwall?

4 What injury did Cathy Gale visit Dr Macombie about?

5 The famous fight for this episode was held in what location?

22 TROJAN HORSE

1 What was the name of the horse that Steed was keeping an eye on?

2 What does Steed eat for lunch at the stables?

3 What is the name of the horse that Cathy Gale bets on in the race being televised?

4 What is the name of the crooked major?

5 What kind of class is being given in the stables that is overheard by Steed?

23 THE OUTSIDE-IN MAN

1 What is the name of the agent who comes back from the dead?

2 Where is Mr Quilpie's office located?

3 In which department does Steed work under Mr Quilpie?

4 Where did Cathy Gale keep her gun?

5 What kind of bones did Steed get from the butcher?

6 What item is on Mr Quilpie's desk for every interview?

24 THE CHARMERS

1 What was the name of the establishment where Steed discovered an enemy agent in a coffin of bowler hats?

2 What was the name of the enemy agent who broke into Steed's apartment?

3 Where does Kim Lawrence tell Steed she has hidden the head of a dead body?

4 Where was Steed when George Vinkel was killed?

5 In which area of London was the charm school located?

6 What three-term motto is used for the enemy identification board?

7 What is Kim Lawrence's profession?

25 ESPRIT DE CORPS

1 How many bullets from different rifles were fired at Corporal Craig?

2 What regiment is featured?

3 What brand of Champagne is mentioned in the name of General Sir Ian Stuart?

4 What became Cathy Gale's code-name?

5 How was Steed saved from execution?

26 LOBSTER QUADRILLE

1 What was the name of the villain who was hiding for drug smuggling?

2 Where was Jonathan Williams found?

3 What item did Cathy Gale investigate that was found in Williams' belongings?

4 What did Steed do to the champagne that he didn't like at the restaurant?

5 To what island is Cathy Gale heading at the end of the episode?

Points Available: **69**
Your current score: _____

#27 - QUICK TEST - SERIES 3

1 What is the name of Steed's superior who issued him with the assignment into a plot of doubles found in a holiday camp?

    A) Charles   *B) Eric*   *C) Ernie*

2 Which episode uses the millionaires' rest home called Adelphi Park?

    A) The   *B) The*   *C) The*
    Underground   *Undertakers*   *Underwhelmed*

3 In which episode did Steed have two old ladies helping him around the houses of Parliament?

    A) January Two   *B) December Six*   *C) November Five*

4 Who was the contact Steed visited as he tried to find Hal Anderson in 'The Wringer'?

    A) Lovell   *B) Duffel*   *C) Muffel*

5 Where is 'November Five' set?

    A) Big Ben   *B) The Houses*   *C) Buckingham*
                of Parliament   *Palace*

6 What is the name of Steed's dog in 'Death of a Batman'?

    A) Katie   *B) Cathy*   *C) Kayleigh*

7 What fictional character did Steed refer to as a 'bright little feller' in the episode 'Man With Two Shadows'?

    A) Binbin   *B) Sinsin*   *C) Tintin*

Points Available: **7**
Your current score: ____

#28 - Avengers Sudoku 1

Complete the picture pattern using the key below.

S = Steed

K = David Keel

C = Cathy Gale

E = Emma Peel

T = Tara King

P = Purdey

G = Mike Gambit

M = Mother

R = Rhonda

Points Available: **10**

Your current score: _____

#29 - Under The Hat 5 - Series 3

1 Honor Blackman was supposed to cry when Cathy Gale was confronted by Martin Goodman – true or false?

2 Honor Blackman had a liaison with Sean Connery – true or false?

3 Honor Blackman could ride a motorcycle before doing so for *The Avengers* – true or false?

4 A movie version of *The Avengers* was planned to star Patrick Macnee and Honor Blackman in 1964 – true or false?

5 There were two different opening title sequences for Series 3 – true or false?

Points Available: **5**

Your current score: ____

#30 - Mrs Catherine Gale

1 What was the occupation of Mrs Catherine Gale?

2 What episode has Cathy Gale standing for parliament to expose a scandal involving the recently murdered MP Michael Dyter?

3 What is Cathy Gale's date of birth?

4 Cathy Gale did the ton plus ten in which episode?

5 In which episode does Cathy Gale have to wear an eye patch in Act Three after a fight in a printer's shop?

6 What knowledge did Cathy Gale show to Steed's superior, Charles, in '*Man With Two Shadows*'?

7 In which part of the world did Cathy Gale live with her late husband?

8 How did Cathy preserve Steed's cover in '*The Little Wonders*'?

9 What is Cathy Gale aware of with Steed when she is wined and dined well?

10 Where does Cathy Gale live?

Points Available: **10**
Your current score: _____

#31 - Episodic Trivia - Series 4 - Part A

1 THE MURDER MARKET

1 What is the name of the marriage bureau?

2 How does Steed prepare Emma Peel's coffin?

3 What activity does Steed engage in on his date with Barbara Wakefield?

4 Where is Barbara Wakefield from?

5 Who turned out to be the marriage bureau's managing director?

2 THE MASTER MINDS

1 Where was the headquarters of Ransack?

2 What is stolen by the students of Ransack?

3 How much did Emma Peek add onto Steed's test to make him qualify for genius level?

4 What was Steed's suggestion to aid the plan to steal the aeroplane from the security establishment?

5 Where did Steed place his test paper answers for his exam?

6 What physical apparatus does Emma Peel enjoy as Steed explains about the theft of a missile?

7 Who was the villain behind the projection screen?

3   DIAL A DEADLY NUMBER

1   How fast did Steed arrive on the scene after the death of Norman Todhunter?

2   What was the weapon being used to kill the company chairmen of Boardman's?

3   How does Steed defeat John Harvey?

4   What wine is given to Steed during the wine cellar test?

5   What did Fitch design to kill Steed?

6   What weapon are Steed and Emma Peel threatened with by Fitch?

7   What is Henry Boardman's profession?

4   DEATH AT BARGAIN PRICES

1   Where in the store is the bomb placed by King Kane?

2   What was the name of the department store?

3   What science is Emma Peel studying when Steed interrupts her?

4   How do Steed and Emma Peel end the episode?

5   What is the name of the kidnapped Professor?

6   What would a customer have to buy to set off the bomb?

7   What injury is Steed nursing after his visit to King Kane?

5 TOO MANY CHRISTMAS TREES

1 What was the profession of Brandon Storey?

2 What caused Freddie Marshall's death?

3 On which Dickens story is Steed's costume based?

4 Which colleague does Steed dream about being dead, only for Emma Peel to confirm it?

5 To which part of the Ministry is Dr Felix Teasel revealed to be attached?

6 What number is underneath Freddie Marshall's picture?

7 In which room does Emma Peel discover the body of Jeremy Wade?

8 What form of ESP is being used against Steed?

9 Who sends Steed a Christmas card from Fort Knox?

10 In what jar does Steed keep his sugar?

6 THE CYBERNAUTS

1 What was the name of the company headed by Dr Clement Armstrong?

2 What characteristic does Steed notice about the killer of Lambert?

3 What was different about how Samuel Hammond was killed?

4 How many Cybernauts fight at the end of the episode?

5 What item guided the Cybernauts?

6 What curious sound does a Cybernaut's chop make?

7 What equipment can be found in the handle of Steed's umbrella?

8 Who was the scientist who aided Dr Clement Armstrong?

7 THE GRAVEDIGGERS

1 What was the name of the professor who was believed dead but was actually alive?

2 What is Emma Peel tied to?

3 What is Sir Horace Winslip mad about?

4 What is hidden in the coffins?

5 What organisation does Steed claim to represent when he is found in the hospital by Sager?

8 ROOM WITHOUT A VIEW

1 What was the time in the concentration camp that was remembered by both Steed and scientist John Wadkin?

2 What was the name of the man who was insistent upon seeing Dr Cullen?

3 In which camp was John Wadkin a prisoner?

4 What floor is the room actually on?

5 What was the cover Steed used to get into the presence of Max Chessman?

9 A SURFEIT OF H2O

1 What is the name of the wine that Steed prefers and gets bottles of?

2 What was the name of poacher Ted Barker's brother?

3 What natural element was used as a weapon?

4 Who does Steed claim to be working for when he visits Dr Sturm's wine factory?

5 Where is Emma Peel trapped?

10 Two's A Crowd

1 What is the name of the car that needed an oil change?

2 What is the alias used by Steed to infiltrate the team?

3 What is the anagram of Pudeshkin, Schvedlof, Elena and Vogel?

4 What is the liquor that Steed hands to Brodny in the bar?

5 What is accidentally placed onto the carnation at the party?

11 Man Eater Of Surrey Green

1 What is the name of the sweet lady botanist who assists Steed and Emma in their investigation?

2 Who were the other three scientists to join Laura Burford in mysteriously going missing in Surrey Green?

3 In what subject is Laura Burford an expert?

4 What device protects Alan Carter and Miss Sheldon?

5 Which controlled person does Steed physically fight for the herbicide?

12 SILENT DUST

1 What is the name of the scrumpy-loving villain?

2 What does Steed hallucinate Emma to be when he is shot?

3 What activity are Steed and Emma Peel doing when they're first seen?

4 Who spies on Steed and Emma Peel from a tree?

5 What was Peter Omrod's profession?

13 THE TOWN OF NO RETURN

1 What was the name of the town that was being over-run by enemy agents?

2 What cake did Steed offer to Emma Peel as they made their way down by train?

3 What did Mark Brandon say to Emma Peel before he died?

4 How did Steed treat Piggy Warren's moustache when trying to get information on Emma's whereabouts?

5 What ride did Steed play on in the playground?

Points Available: **79**

Your current score: ____

#32 – AVENGING ACRONYMS

Secret societies; devious departments and menacing machines - they all need a memorable and concise name. Can you spell out the following acronyms?

1 What is DISCO?

2 What is the QQF?

3 What is the BEB?

4 What is UFD?

5 What is GONN?

6 What is BIG BEN?

7 What is PURR?

8 What is PANSAC?

9 What is MOT NRU?

10 What is SNOB?

Points Available: 10
Your current score: _____

#33 - Episodic Trivia - Series 4 - Part B

14 The Hour That Never Was

1 What is the name of the base visited by Steed and Emma?

2 What unconscious animal is found by Emma Peel underneath the aeroplane?

3 What morning item do Steed and Emma Peel finish the episode on?

4 For what occasion was the gift that Steed gave to Geoffrey Risdale, only to be discovered smashed?

5 What did Steed crash his Bentley into?

6 At what time are all the clocks stopped?

7 What character is shot and then mysteriously disappears?

8 What kind of person does Steed meet when searching for Emma Peel?

15 Castle De'ath

1 What was the name of the Laird?

2 What is Black Jamie?

3 What feature accessed the secret chambers?

4 Emma Peel represents what organisation?

5 How much taller was the frogman after being on the rack?

6 What instrument does Black Jamie play?

16 THE THIRTEENTH HOLE

1 What weapon was used to deal with Ted Murphy?

2 What sport is being played?

3 Where does the action take place?

4 What hat is Steed wearing as he keeps an eye on Dr Adams?

5 What is the name of the satellite passing over?

6 What times must Dr Adams always tee off?

17 SMALL GAME FOR BIG HUNTERS

1 What was the name of the sickness reportedly coming in from Kalaya?

2 What sandwiches did Steed have in his Bentley?

3 What strain of fly was going to be used to spread the sickness?

4 Where was Jack Kendrick found?

5 What are Steed and Emma doing at the end of the episode?

18 THE GIRL FROM AUNTIE

1 Who are the brothers who outfitted Georgie Price Jones?

2 What kind of party does Emma Peel attend?

3 How did the killer get around?

4 Which organisation kidnaps Emma Peel?

5 Who is the agent bidding for Emma who tangles with Steed?

19 QUICK-QUICK SLOW DEATH

1 What was found in the pram?

2 What decorative item was on the killer's arm?

3 What does Steed claim to have lost when being interviewed by Lucille?

4 Whose face does the band wear at the gala night?

5 Who is Emma Peel's chirpy colleague at the dance school?

20 THE DANGER MAKERS

1 What was Steed's code-name?

2 What colour of Rose was used?

3 Who was Apollo?

4 Which soldier put Steed onto Manton House?

5 What were the danger makers planning on stealing?

21 A TOUCH OF BRIMSTONE

1 What, according to Steed, was found in an Ambassadors soup?

2 What is the golden rule of drinking from a glass in the Hellfire Club?

3 Who did Steed duel with?

4 What is the name of Steed's hangover cure?

5 What did Cartney make Emma into as midnight approached?

22 WHAT THE BUTLER SAW

1 What were Steed's aliases after visiting the double agent barber?

2 Who was the villain?

3 Why was Hemming killed?

4 Where are the miniature tape recorders hidden by Benson?

5 What game were Emma Peel and Group Captain Miles caught playing?

23 THE HOUSE THAT JACK BUILT

1 What was the object used by Emma to destroy the house?

2 What bursts Steed's tyres?

3 How long did doctors give Professor Jack Keller?

4 What kind of device was found in the door frame of the study?

5 What kind of properties did the key possess?

24 A SENSE OF HISTORY

1 What was the name of the University?

2 Who was the leader of the rebel students?

3 What is the students nickname for Dr Henge?

4 What outfit is worn by both Emma and Dubuoys at the ball?

5 What character are Steed and Emma Peel told to look out for by Marianne?

25 HOW TO SUCCEED... AT MURDER

1 What was the surname of Henry and Henrietta?

2 What is Henrietta?

3 What was Henrietta?

4 What was the name of the perfume identified by J.J. Hooter?

5 What is the slogan for all of the ladies at the keep fit class?

26 HONEY FOR THE PRINCE

1 Who was called the mystical star of the East?

2 What game does Prince Ali play with Steed?

3 Who is the owner of the honey shop?

4 What dance does Emma Peel perform?

5 What was Ronnie Wescott's fantasy?

Points Available: **70**
Your current score: _____

#34 - Quick Test - Series 4 - Part 1

1 What was the name of the Ambassador who featured in the episode '*Two's A Crowd*' and was played by Warren Mitchell?

    A) Brody   *B) Brodny*   *C) Brady*

2 Julian Glover played which letter of the fictitious Colonel Psev in the episode '*Two's A Crowd*'?

    A) P   *B) S*   *C) V*

3 What is the code-name of agent Frederick Withers?

    A) Pingo   *B) Bingo*   *C) Pongo*

4 What particular toy is the obsession of Colonel Psev?

    A) Toy Cars   *B) Toy Aeroplanes*   *C) Toy Soldiers*

5 What game board was used for the Series 4 USA opening titles?

    A) Chalk Board   *B) Chess Board*   *C) Cheese Board*

6 Who tried to alert Steed to the identity of Colonel Psev before he was killed in '*Two's A Crowd*'?

    A) Ivenko   *B) Gordon Webster*   *C) Major Plessy*

Points Available: **6**
Your current score: _____

#35 - 'ELLO, STEED; GOT A NEW MOTOR?

A	V	W	A	N	Z	M	B	Y	L	O	B	D	E	E
P	D	F	R	A	N	G	E	R	O	V	E	R	C	P
O	L	S	Y	Q	B	J	B	S	T	N	S	H	K	U
R	I	Y	A	H	Q	A	Q	A	U	F	D	W	L	O
U	O	G	B	K	A	R	E	B	S	R	B	F	N	C
E	J	D	C	E	H	O	O	N	E	A	N	C	M	R
S	H	S	J	L	N	S	K	Q	L	S	J	A	R	A
U	G	T	K	Q	K	T	M	I	A	N	K	B	T	U
T	D	A	L	G	P	E	L	N	N	A	L	D	I	G
O	S	J	Q	A	E	G	M	E	M	C	C	J	K	A
L	B	R	O	L	L	S	R	O	Y	C	E	L	M	J
F	H	K	N	G	D	T	P	G	N	O	W	D	E	K
J	K	W	T	A	W	D	O	D	A	B	C	A	S	A
K	P	Q	U	M	K	A	L	X	S	R	A	T	T	L
S	J	X	R	A	U	G	A	J	P	A	D	M	Z	F

Steed and his colleagues drove a number of vehicles over the years. Can you find them all?

BENTLEY	JAGUAR XJS
RANGE ROVER	LOTUS ELAN
LOTUS EUROPA	JAGUAR COUPE
ROLLS ROYCE	AC COBRA

Points Available: **8**
Your current score: _____

1 Who shot Steed in '*Silent Dust*'?

    A) Mellors   *B) Juggins*   *C) Beryl Snow*

2 Who is the traitorous scientist in '*The Thirteenth Hole*'?

    A) Dr Adams   *B) Dr Keel*   *C) Dr King*

3 Who is the villain in '*A Sense of History*'?

    A) Grindley   *B) Friar Tuck*   *C) Robin Hood*

4 What caused Steed to crash his car in '*The Hour That Never Was*'?

    A) His steering wheel   *B) A dog*   *C) Faulty brakes*

5 What substance filled the room during Steed's fight in '*The Hour That Never Was*'?

    A) Knockout gas   *B) Laughing gas*   *C) Gas and air*

6 What was the cause of the drownings in the field in '*A Surfeit of H2O*'?

    A) Torrential rain   *B) A heatwave*   *C) A tap*

7 What does Steed manually raise in '*The Cybernauts*'?

    A) His bowler   *B) His umbrella*   *C) The heating*

Points Available: 7
Your current score: ____

#37 - BEHIND THE SCENES - SERIES 4

1 Name the composer of *The Avengers* theme from Series 4 to 6?

    A) Laurie Metcalf   *B) Laurie Latham*   *C) Laurie Johnson*

2 What was writer Philip Levene's former profession before he became a script writer?

    A) Tea Boy   *B) Worker in a*   *C) Scientist*
                    pathological morgue

3 Which Series 4 episode featured heavily in the 1998 movie?

    A) The Murder   *B) A Surfeit*   *C) Honey For*
      Market   *of H2O*   *The Prince*

4 Diana Rigg was known primarily for working in what entertainment medium?

    A) Television   *B) Theatre*   *C) Literature*

5 Who designed Emma Peel's wardrobe in Series 4?

    A) John Bates   *B) John Frieda*   *C) John Stewart*

6 Which episode was banned in America?

    A) A Touch   *B) Dial A*   *C) The Girl*
  of Brimstone   *Deadly Number*   *From Auntie*

Points Available: **6**
Your current score: ____

#38 – Under The Hat 6 – Series 4

1 Diana Rigg is the only person to have married James Bond – true or false?

2 Diana Rigg was from Yorkshire – true or false?

3 Patrick Macnee won the 'Best Dressed Male' award twice – true or false?

4 Laurie Johnson also composed the TV theme for *This is Your Life* – true or false?

5 Diana Rigg's first series was in black and white – true or false?

6 Diana Rigg designed the costume for her appearance as the Queen of Sin in '*A Touch of Brimstone*' – true or false?

7 The make of watch carried by Steed in '*Dial A Deadly Number*' is a Rolex – true or false?

Points Available: 5
Your current score: ____

#39 - Episodic Trivia - Series 5 - Part A

1 THE FEAR MERCHANTS

1 What is the villain Pemberton scared of?

2 Where was Richard Meadows found?

3 In what location did Steed fight Gilbert?

4 What character had a fear of spiders?

5 What is Steed's fear?

6 What cover did Steed use when he visited Fox, White and Crawley?

2 ESCAPE IN TIME

1 Which era did Emma Peel find herself trapped in when undergoing torture at the hands of Matthew Thyssen?

2 Where was the location that Steed and Emma Peel found Colonel Josino and began following them?

3 What domestic duty did Steed learn about Emma Peel?

4 What colour is Colonel Josino's crocodile?

5 What animal did Steed claim to hear in the background while he was being taken to Thyssen?

3 THE BIRD WHO KNEW TOO MUCH

1 What is the name of the courier who is taking the information of Muswell's Back out of the country?

2 What was the name of Captain Crusoe's owner?

3 Why does Steed keep straps on his car bonnet?

4 Which stuntman performed the dive from the diving board?

5 What did Steed use to fight Cunliffe?

6 What musical note is Captain Crusoe's triangle?

7 What is the drink that Steed offers to his friends after they have been tied up and are facing a lethal booby trap?

8 Where was the residence of Captain Crusoe?

9 What was Captain Crusoe?

10 What device was placed into Steed's umbrella by enemy agent Verret?

4 FROM VENUS WITH LOVE

1 Who are the BVS?

2 What colour are the victims turned to?

3 Who was recording a play of his memoirs?

4 What test did Dr Primble give to Steed as an eye test?

5 What weapon was being used by the villains?

5 THE SEE-THROUGH MAN

1 What was the name of the scientist who had apparently come up with the means of making someone invisible?

2 What is the name of Major Vazin's wife?

3 How does Emma Peel disarm Brodny?

4 What attacks Brodny after his fall?

5 What number was the file that was stolen from the records room?

6 THE WINGED AVENGER

1 Who were the publishers being targeted?

2 What was the sound of The Winged Avenger?

3 What is the name of Sir Lexius Cray's butler?

4 To which American superhero and his TV series was homage paid in the fight on the ceiling?

5 Who was the artist who supplied the drawings for the episode?

6 Who turned out to be The Winged Avenger?

7 THE LIVING DEAD

1 Mandy Mackay is a member of what organisation?

2 Rupert is the 15th Duke of what?

3 What was the name of the vagrant Steed visited to get information?

4 What word did Steed refer to as somebody's wine stock but panicked Masgard who thought he was talking about something else?

5 How did Masgard trap himself and the other enemy agents in the underground city?

8 THE HIDDEN TIGER

1 The villain was what domestic animal?

2 How does Cheshire drink his milk when talking to Steed?

3 What is the name of the component that Steed finds which transmits brainwaves?

4 Which victim used to keep a pet lion?

5 Which part of the directory is Steed looking for when he arrives at Emma Peel's apartment?

6 What kind of cat did Steed describe to Cheshire, calling her Emma?

9 THE CORRECT WAY TO KILL

1 What was the name of the organisation being used as a front to train enemy agents?

2 What was the name of the partner Steed was given by Nutski?

3 What was the place visited by Emma Peel and Ivan, only for Ivan to disappear?

4 How does Olga describe hard liquor?

5 Who was the first victim found by Steed and Emma Peel?

10 NEVER, NEVER SAY DIE

1 What was the name of the victim who kept being knocked down and coming back to life?

2 How far was the victim thrown?

3 How many times is the victim hit by the car?

4 What item keeps being destroyed?

5 What does Emma notice about the confined Professor Stone, confirming that he is the genuine article?

11 EPIC

1 What was the name of the actor who kidnapped Emma Peel in a taxi?

2 Who was the film director?

3 Where does the action take place for Emma Peel?

4 What famous film studio logo did Emma Peel mimic?

5 What is Emma Peel tied to for her final scene?

12 THE SUPERLATIVE SEVEN

1 Where is the fancy dress party held?

2 What toy does Emma Peel use to summon Steed?

3 What astrological star sign is uttered by Emma Peel as she reveals the double of the killer?

4 How many coffins are awaiting the guests?

5 What is Steed's costume?

Points Available: **68**
Your current score: ____

#40 - Crossword 3

Across

2 Episode title; involving black magic (7)

5 *A La Carte, On The Rocks* and *of a Batman* (5)

6 Episode title; Immortal ____ (4)

8 Catherine Gale was trapped here in '*Don't Look Behind You*' (5)

9 Profession of villains repeated in '*The Gravediggers*' (10)

Down

1 Christian name of Dr Keel (5)

3 Surname of the actress who played Catherine Gale (8)

4 Surname of the actor who played John Steed (6)

7 First name of the actress who played Catherine Gale (5)

Points Available: **9**

Anagram answer: _____ (1 extra point)

Your current score: ____

#41 - Episodic Trivia - Series 5 - Part B

13 A Funny Thing Happened On The Way To The Station

1 Who was in charge of the organisation that was trying to kill the Prime Minister?

2 What clue did Steed leave for Emma Peel when he disappeared?

3 What mode of transport was the setting for this episode?

4 What are two people dressed as when they're occupying a train carriage in pursuit of the briefcase belonging to Steed's contact, Lucas?

5 Who are Steed and Emma Peel trying to avoid at the end?

14 Something Nasty In The Nursery

1 What was the name of the ball?

2 Which target had the nickname of cuddles?

3 What was the name of the nanny everyone kept seeing?

4 What was the name of the toy shop?

5 What was the scent that all the targets remember and was noticed by Emma Peel when they found Dobson?

15 THE JOKER

1 Who was Emma Peel's tormentor?

2 Some of the doors are designed to look like what?

3 What was the song used to serenade Emma Peel?

4 What location is Emma Peel trapped in?

5 What room did the strange young man tell Emma Peel to look inside?

6 What game is being played by Steed at the end?

16 WHO'S WHO???

1 The agents who swap identities with Steed and Emma Peel are Basil and who?

2 What colours are the dice being used by Basil?

3 Which floral agent was Major B's right hand?

4 Which floral agent was also a writer for *The Avengers* series?

5 What kind of headache transfers from Basil to Steed when they've switched?

17 DEATH'S DOOR

1 What was the last image seen by the victims of the nightmares?

2 Who saw the lion in his nightmare before he died?

3 What happened to Steed when he visited Albert Becker?

4 What mechanical fault caused Steed's car to career off the road?

5 What did Emma Peel's horoscope predict for her?

6 What does Steed hope that Lord Melford isn't when he changes the calendar date?

18 RETURN OF THE CYBERNAUTS

1 What was the relationship between Paul Beresford and Dr Clement Armstrong?

2 Which scientist tries to escape from Paul Beresford?

3 What item controlled Emma Peel?

4 How is the Cybernaut being directed?

5 In what three ways did Paul want Steed and Emma Peel dealt with?

19 Dead Man's Treasure

1 What is the final clue to George Benstead's treasure hunt?

2 Who is Steed's partner in the treasure hunt?

3 What is the colour of the treasure chest?

4 What is delivered when the bell rang on the racing simulator?

5 What is the name of the agent Steed is waiting up for?

6 What time does Emma Peel arrive at Steed's flat?

7 How many enemy agents are in pursuit of Steed and Emma Peel?

8 What setting is unique on Steed's shaving razor?

20 THE £50,000 BREAKFAST

1 What is the breed of dogs?

2 What is the name of the puppet found by Steed?

3 What is the name of the man who had the driving accident?

4 Who, according to Emma Peel, is the tough one out of the villains?

5 What is the name of the butler?

21 YOU HAVE JUST BEEN MURDERED

1 What is the name of the villain?

2 What kind of person is targeted?

3 What kind of millionaire does Steed become?

4 Who was the first victim?

5 What did George Unwin place into his briefcase for the blackmailer?

22 MURDERSVILLE

1 What family members did Emma Peel announce to Steed when trying to acquire his help?

2 Where was Major Paul Croft making his new home?

3 What was the name of the doctor?

4 Where was Emma Peel placed in a bid by the village to force her to talk?

5 How many people are imprisoned in the museum with Emma Peel?

23 THE POSITIVE-NEGATIVE MAN

1 What does Steed get stuck to?

2 What number was the project?

3 What grade is Cynthia Wentworth-Howe?

4 What kind of power is on display and being used to kill the victims?

5 What is the name of the research centre?

24 MISSION... HIGHLY IMPROBABLE

1 Which villain was an Admiral the last time Steed saw him?

2 What is Steed shrunken inside of?

3 What is the name of the doctor using the shrinking device?

4 What is the first thing to disappear as it's being escorted from the main gate?

5 What is the name of Steed's security colleague who disappears down a drain?

#42 - Miss Tara King

1 Miss Tara King used to carry what in her handbag?

2 In which episode did Tara King use ether and potassium chloride to escape confinement?

3 Who is Charles Merrydale?

4 Tara King played the trumpet for the very first time brilliantly in what episode?

5 What did Tara King have an assortment of?

6 What part of the emergency service was in Tara King's flat?

7 What is Tara King's address?

8 What is Tara's trainee agent number when she first meets John Steed?

9 What does Tara give to Steed when she introduces herself?

10 What was the disguise that Tara used in her first mission with Steed in '*Invasion of the Earthmen*'?

Points Available: **10**
Your current score: ____

#43 - Under The Hat 7 - Series 5

1 Diana Rigg was a Dame – true or false?

2 *The Avengers* was filmed next door to ITC series *The Saint* – true or false?

3 Diana Rigg's daughter is also an actress – true or false?

4 *The Avengers* was the first UK television series to be shown on 'prime time' in the USA – true or false?

5 Diana Rigg was the only cast member of *The Avengers* to appear with Morecambe and Wise – true or false?

Points Available: **5**
Your current score: ____

#44 - QUICK TEST - SERIES 5

1 In which episode did Steed have to be rescued by Emma Peel after he was caught and tied to a chair?

    A) The Living Dead   *B) The Hidden Tiger*   *C) The Superlative Seven*

2 What is Captain Crusoe?

    A) A racehorse   *B) A parrot*   *C) A sailor*

3 Which episode has the tag scene featuring Steed and Emma on an actual film set?

    A) Death's Door   *B) Epic*   *C) From Venus With Love*

4 Which episode first featured Steed's answer phone?

    A) The Fear Merchants   B) The Bird Who Knew Too Much   C) Epic

5 Where is the party held in 'The Superlative Seven'?

    A) A train   B) A plane   C) A theme park

6 How does Steed summon Mrs Peel?

    A) We're Wanted   B) We're In Trouble   C) We're Needed

7 What does Emma Peel suggest when Steed asks for her choice of coffee or orange juice in 'Death's Door'?

    A) Coffee   B) Orange Juice   C) Both

8 Which deadly robots from series 4 made their reappearance?

    A) The Man-Eating plant   B) Colonel Psev   C) The Cybernauts

9 What colour is Steed's Bentley?

    A) Blue   B) Green   C) Red

10 Emma Peel experiments in what field?

    A) Mathematics   B) Science   C) A field of buttercups

Points Available: **10**

Your current score: ____

#45 - CONUNDRUM 4

This person has been in space, the dales... But they stopped in Avengerland first;

DAN H SLINTORO

Who is it?

_ _ _ _ _ _   _ _ _ _ _ _ _ _

Points Available: **1**

Your current score: ____

#46 - Behind The Scenes - Series 5

1 What was the writing pseudonym used for *The Avengers* episode '*A Funny Thing Happened on The Way to The Station*'?

    A) Brian Marshall   *B) Brian Copper*   *C) Brian Sheriff*

2 What colour is Emma Peel's gun as she shoots the cork from the bottle in the Series 5 opening titles?

    A) Gold   *B) Silver*   *C) Bronze*

3 Which musician from the band *Yes* was a session musician on *The Avengers*?

    A) Rick Wakeman   *B) Jon Anderson*   *C) Trevor Horn*

4 Who is Brian Sheriff?

    A) Brian Clemens   *B) Brian Clemens & Roger Marshall*   *C) Roger Marshall*

5 What was the title of the US promotional clip to advertise *The Avengers* arriving in colo(u)r?

    A) A Kill In Colour   *B) The Strange Case of the Missing Corpse*   *C) Kaleidoscope*

6 Diana Rigg was nominated for two Emmy awards as Emma Peel during series 5; but who won them?

    A) Lucille Ball   *B) Barbara Bain*   *C) Jane Fonda*

7 What is the name of the director of the episodes '*The Correct Way To Kill*' and '*False Witness*', who went onto direct the movie *A Fish Called Wanda*?

    A) Charles Bronson   *B) Charles Crichton*   *C) Charles Chaplin*

Points Available: **7**
Your current score: ____

#47 – Episodic Trivia – Series 6 – Part A

1   THE FORGET-ME-KNOT

1   Who was the traitor?

2   For how many weeks had Sean Mortimer been missing?

3   Who wants to put Steed's name on the suspect list when he fails to report in?

4   How many motorbikes are seen by Sean Mortimer?

5   What is the name of Mother's grounds man?

6   What were Steed and Emma Peel doing before they discovered Sean Mortimer?

7   Who is Peter Peel dressed as when he collects Emma from Steed's apartment?

8   What drink does Steed ask for in the hospital?

2   INVASION OF THE EARTHMEN

1   What is the name of the academy?

2   What does Steed advise Tara King to do with an opponent provided the item is double glazed?

3   What kills Grant?

4   How does Steed discover the acid lake?

5   What colour is Tara King's bathrobe?

6   What character did the astronaut resemble when Tara King noticed him in the window behind the blackboard?

3 THE CURIOUS CASE OF THE COUNTLESS CLUES

1 What is the name of Steed's old flame?

2 How did Tara King hurt her leg?

3 What was in the basket that Steed brought to Tara, which she later used against the murderous Earle and Gardiner?

4 What game are Steed and Sir William Burgess playing while Steed is questioning him?

5 What happens to Steed's bowler?

6 Who is the first victim of Earle and Gardiner?

4 SPLIT!

1 What was the name of the enemy agent who was apparently coming back to life?

2 Which ministry was being attacked?

3 What was the name of the hospital?

4 What kind of specialist do Steed and Tara King visit with the notepad?

5 What was Tara King's drink request at the end?

6 How does Steed disarm Hinnel during the fight?

7 Where on the body did Steed shoot Boris Kartovski?

8 Who is the third experiment?

9 In which year did Steed shoot Boris Kartovski?

10 Who arrives by helicopter?

5 GET-A-WAY

1 What was the location of the three enemy agents?

2 What brand is the vodka?

3 What gun does Ezdorf ask to kill Steed with?

4 What colour are the outfits that the enemy agents Rostov, Lubin and Ezdorf are wearing, respectively?

5 Who were the enemy agents' targets?

6 HAVE GUNS – WILL HAGGLE

1 What was the name of the Colonel Steed had to deal with?

2 What is the make of the rifles?

3 How did the thieves get into the establishment?

4 What is the name of the lady selling the stolen rifles?

5 What colour is the sash that Steed finds in the Colonel's quarters?

7 LOOK (STOP ME IF YOU'VE HEARD THIS ONE...) BUT THERE WERE THESE TWO FELLERS

1 What was the name of the clown causing all the killings?

2 What object did Steed and Tara King use to identify the face of the clown?

3 What does the sign read on Steed's back at the end?

4 Who was issuing the orders to the villains?

5 What item did the mute clown Jennings use to communicate?

6 How many costume changes does Merry Maxie Martin go through in his fight with Steed?

7 What clue did Tara King give to Steed when they were debating the red ping pong ball?

8 What flavour is the pie that tries to kill Lord Dessington?

8 MY WILDEST DREAM

1 What is the name of the doctor?

2 Who is the jealous suitor of Tara King who wants Steed out of the way?

3 What object is thrown at the window of Steed's apartment?

4 What are Steed and Tara being used as?

5 What kind of therapy is being practised?

9 WHOEVER SHOT POOR GEORGE OBLIQUE STROKE XR40?

1 What was used to poison George?

2 What accent does Tara King adopt during her cover?

3 What cover does Tara King use to gain entry to Sir Wilfred Pelley's home?

4 What is the last ingredient of the explosive cocktail?

5 How was Tara King set to be killed when her cover was blown?

6 Which member of Sir Wilfred Pelly's household did Steed tell Tara to trust?

7 Who was sabotaging George in the lab?

10 YOU'LL CATCH YOUR DEATH

1 What is the name of the academy sending out the deadly letters?

2 Who is Mother's superior?

3 What are the only two species that suffer from colds, according to Colonel Timothy?

4 What is Tara King placed into during her confinement?

5 What temperature is Tara King's room set to?

11 ALL DONE WITH MIRRORS

1 Where does Steed take Tara King to dinner?

2 What is Mother's headquarters?

3 Who partnered Tara King while Steed was under house arrest?

4 What was the mistake made by the villains when they sent Tara King over the cliff?

5 What seafaring item is used as the villains' headquarters?

6 What came out of the air over the cliffs?

7 What element was allowing the eavesdropping to occur?

12 SUPER SECRET CYPHER SNATCH

1 What is the name of the window cleaning company?

2 What does Tara King go undercover as?

3 According to Steed, what piece of a window cleaner's equipment should never be left unattended?

4 What is the name of the missing agent?

5 What department ended up handling the case at Cypher HQ first?

13 GAME

1   What is Tara trapped in as bait to make Steed rescue her?

2   What is the real name of the villain Monty Bristow?

3   The pieces of what kind of puzzle are left with the victims for Steed and Tara King to find?

4   What part is missing from Steed's Aunt Emily's battered alarm clock?

5   What board game are Steed and Tara King playing at the end of the episode?

6   How many dice men get involved in the fight with Steed and Tara King ?

7   What army rank is Wishforth-Brown?

8   What board game is first sent to Steed?

14 FALSE WITNESS

1   What drink is the cause of everyone telling lies?

2   What is Mother's headquarters?

3   With whom is Steed partnered to find a problem in the assignment against Lord Edgefield?

4   What does Steed do to agent Melville after being lied to?

5   What is the problem with Mother's abdomen?

6   Which ill-fated agent partnered Melville before Steed?

7   What was the name of the company delivering milk?

8   What was Tara King placed into and trapped inside as Steed rounded up the villains?

15 NOON DOOMSDAY

1 What was the department that was housing the injured Steed?

2 Who arrives by helicopter?

3 Who occupied Steed's apartment while he was away?

4 Who is the bedridden agent who gives assistance to Tara King as she defends the house?

5 Where does Steed conceal a weapon?

16 LEGACY OF DEATH

1 What was bequeathed to Steed?

2 What was the name of the special place Steed used to hide the dagger?

3 What toy is Steed playing with?

4 What are the names of the unusual duo who are seeking the dagger?

5 What colour is the pearl that everyone wants?

#48 - John Steed - Part 1

1 According to the stage play, what is John Steed's full name?

2 Where does Steed get his bowlers?

3 In the Cathy Gale era, what is Steed's address?

4 What was the name of Steed's Dalmatian dog?

5 What was the name of the club that Steed had apparently been black-balled from?

6 Which of Steed's aunts sends him rock cakes in the post?

7 What is the wood used for Steed's umbrellas?

8 What animal does Steed proudly keep at his house in *The New Avengers*?

9 What is the one thing that can always be found at Steed's June 13th parties?

10 What is Steed's collar size?

Points Available: **10**
Your current score: _____

17 THEY KEEP KILLING STEED

1 What was the location of the enemy agent Arcos?

2 What food item told Tara King that she was dealing with the real Steed?

3 How many Steeds are created?

4 Who asks Tara King to be his wife?

5 What was Mother testing?

6 What organisation was Mother testing a project for?

7 What type of surgery did Arcos specialise in?

8 Which character's house was used for the conference?

18 WISH YOU WERE HERE

1 What was the name of Tara King's Irish uncle, kept prisoner against his will?

2 Where did Tara King make the base of operations in the fight against the hotel staff?

3 What is the name of Mother's nephew?

4 Who was the traitor in the ranks 'helping' Tara King?

5 What signal was Tara King sending using the lights?

19 KILLER

1   What was the name of the agent who partnered Steed while Tara King was on holiday?

2   What does REMAK stand for?

3   Who was the fake contact agent?

4   How were the bodies placed into the graveyard?

5   What is Tara King's present to Steed at the end?

6   In which part of the Eastern hemisphere does Lady Diana tell Steed she worked?

7   How did Lady Diana enter the factory?

8   What drink do Steed and Lady Diana share together?

20 THE ROTTERS

1   What crumbled in Steed's hand to place him onto the path of Wormdoom Limited?

2   What had happened to Tara King's car when she was finally reunited with it?

3   What type of furniture are Steed, Tara King and Mother sitting on as the case is explained?

4   What were the names of the duo killers of Wormdoom Limited?

5   What item was destroyed with Steed underneath it?

21 THE INTERROGATORS

1 What was the name of the fake training course?

2 What does Steed follow to lead him to the location of the fake training course?

3 What is the secret ingredient in Tara King's soup?

4 Who was the Lieutenant who began betraying his informers?

5 How did someone enter Mother's headquarters?

22 THE MORNING AFTER

1 What did Jimmy Merlin steal and give as a gift to Steed?

2 How many hours was Steed asleep for?

3 What did Steed prefer to take as a bribe over English pounds from Jimmy Merlin?

4 What is the name of the Brigadier who caused London to be evacuated?

5 How does Steed describe Jimmy Merlin to Tara King?

23 LOVE ALL

1 What sport is Mother playing during the briefing?

2 Who was the fictional author?

3 Who are the Bellchamber Brothers?

4 What is the hidden instruction at the back of the book?

5 What does Tara King nearly commit in the name of love?

24 TAKE ME TO YOUR LEADER

1 What item was everyone following?

2 What was the animal that was playing courier and observed by Tara King and Captain?

3 What was Steed's cover name when he went to the hotel, as per his instructions?

4 Where was Sally's key hidden?

5 In what place was Tara King trapped and surrounded by several of the cases?

25 STAY TUNED

1 Where did Steed apparently go for three weeks?

2 Who was in charge of the department while Mother was on holiday?

3 Which agent is put in place to keep an eye on Steed?

4 What is the code word to trigger Steed's conditioning?

5 Who is Steed's target?

26 FOG

1 Who was the supposed villain?

2 What weather hampers Steed looking after members of a disarmament committee?

3 Who is Mark Travers' favourite author?

4 What month did the Gaslight Ghoul emerge in 1888?

5 What is the weapon of choice for the Gaslight Ghoul?

27 WHO WAS THAT MAN I SAW YOU WITH?

1 What was the name of the battle computer designed by Steed?

2 Where was the headquarters of enemy agents Zaroff and Dangerfield?

3 What grade was Tara King reduced to during the investigation into her dealings with Zaroff?

4 How long was Steed given to clear Tara King's name?

5 What is the job of Gladys Culpepper?

6 How did Tara King prove her innocence to Steed?

28 PANDORA

1 What is the painting that gets accidentally destroyed?

2 What are the names of the villainous brothers?

3 What type of clock is Tara King interested in buying?

4 Whose files does Steed pass comment on while looking up the fierce rabbit?

5 In what setting are the brothers forcing Tara King to act?

5 In what episode did Mother's assistant finally talk - only to be dubbed in by Mother doing his ventriloquist act?

    A) All Done   B) Homicide and   C) Requiem
    With Mirrors   Old Lace

6 What ingredient does Steed use in his omelette in 'The Rotters'?

    A) Tomato   B) Mushroom   C) Pepper

7 What kind of butter was Tara King trapped inside in 'False Witness'?

    A) Salted   B) Unsalted   C) Low Fat

8 What did Steed construct in 'Who Was That Man I Saw You With?'

    A) A Fort   B) A Champagne Fountain   C) A Rocket

Points Available: 8
Your current score: ____

#52 - JOHN STEED - PART 2

1 In what two colours is Steed's house decorated at different times in *The New Avengers*?

2 Which family member is in the painting above Steed's fireplace in series 3?

3 What particular toys does Steed have that appear in 'The Murder Market' and 'Dirtier By The Dozen'?

4 How many dogs did Steed have over the course of the series?

5 Where did Steed live in the colour series?

6 What does Steed keep in his tuba?

7 How many Bentleys does Steed drive?

8 How does Steed like his tea stirred?

9 What rainy-day item is John Steed never without?

10 What style of hat does John Steed normally wear?

Points Available: **10**
Your current score: _____

#53 - UNDER THE HAT 8 - SERIES 6

1 Linda Thorson is Canadian – true or false?

2 Linda Thorson chose Tara King's name – true or false?

3 Linda Thorson was once in Star Trek – true or false?

4 Patrick Macnee was the last actor from *The Avengers* to appear in a James Bond Movie – true or false?

5 Patrick Macnee often described himself as an 18th-century man – true or false?

Points Available: **5**
Your current score: _____

#54 - Who's Who? - Part 1

1 In the episode 'The Hidden Tiger', which famous comedic actor played the role of Cheshire?

2 Which Hammer horror star appeared as Paul Beresford in 'Return of the Cybernauts' and as Von Claus in The New Avengers episode 'The Eagle's Nest'?

3 Which actor famous for playing Alfred in the Batman movies played the creator of the Cybernauts, Dr Clement Armstrong and then appeared as Nutski in 'The Correct Way To Kill'?

4 Who was the actor who played Ambassador Brodny in the episodes 'Two's a Crowd' and 'The See-Through Man' and played Alf Garnett in the sitcom Till Death Us Do Part?

5 What is the name of the actress who played the villainous Lisa in 'Stay Tuned' and went on to appear as Madame Gerda in *The Avengers* stage play?

6 Which film star appeared in 'Never, Never Say Die' and 'The Interrogators', but is more famous as Count Dooku in *Star Wars* and most famous as Count Dracula?

7 In the episode 'Look (Stop Me If You've Heard This One...) But There Were These Two Fellers', which actor played the jovial Bradley Marler?

8 What was the name of the *Monty Python* star who appeared as Marcus Rugman in the episode 'Look (Stop Me If You've Heard This One...) But There Were These Two Fellers'?

9 Which *Dad's Army* star played Sir George Benstead in the episode 'Dead Man's Treasure'?

10 Which star of the series *Target* played Eric Dubouys in the episode 'A Sense of History'

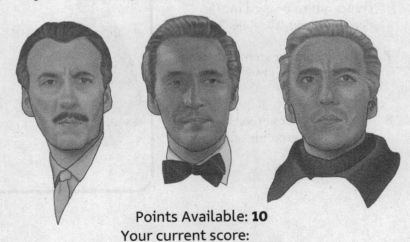

Points Available: **10**
Your current score: _____

#55 - John Steed - Part 3

1 How many sugars does Steed take in his tea?

2 What books does Steed enjoy reading, as seen in 'The Outside-In Man', 'The Rotters' and 'Man With Two Shadows' respectively?

3 What are the collars on Steed's suits made of?

4 What is Steed's regular choice of footwear?

5 At which RAF base was Steed stationed, which he visitef later with Emma Peel to attend its closing down party in 'The Hour That Never Was'?

6 What part of Steed's umbrella comes out to be used in 'The Grandeur That Was Rome'?

7 What decorative item of Steed's was given to him by Emma Peel?

8 What sport does Steed happily enjoy in the grounds of his country home?

9 What item lines Steed's hat?

10 According to Tara King, whose name came up almost every day in her training?

11 Where does Steed usually stay when he visits Paris?

12 Can Steed swim?

13 How old was Steed when he drove point for the lazy tee in '*Hostage*'?

14 According to Steed, how does a connoisseur refer to his wine stock in '*The Living Dead*'?

15 What style of suit does Steed wear?

#56 - WHO'S WHO? - PART 2

1 Who played the bride who threw her bouquet into Steed's bowler when he visited the Togetherness Marriage Bureau in '*The Murder Market*' and later played the school mistress Audrey in '*Take Me To Your Leader*'?

2 Who played Mark Crayford in '*Dead Men Are Dangerous*' and was the first choice to play George Cowley in *The Professionals* and also played the voice of Alfred for two episodes of *Batman: The Animated Series*?

3 Who played the ill-fated character Tom Smallwood in '*The Town of No Return*'; only to come back to the series and play the pivotal role of Mother?

4 Which actor, who later played James Bond's boss M, played a villain in 'The Town of No Return'?

5 Which future star of romantic sitcom *As Time Goes By* played the villains Martin Smythe in 'A Surfeit of H2O' and Dr Paul Bernard in 'Propellant 23'?

6 What is the name of the actor from the *Pink Panther* movies who played King Tenuphon in 'Kill The King' and businessman Mr Tusamo in 'The Cybernauts'?

7 Which star of ITC series *The Champions* appeared as CIA agent Marty Brine in *The New Avengers* episode 'Trap'?

8 Which stage actor and producer appeared as a heavy alongside Ray Austin in the episode 'The Gravediggers'?

9 Which actor from sitcoms *The Good Life* and *Yes, Minister* appeared as Lord William Beaumont in 'Something Nasty in The Nursery'?

10 Which actor played Vogel in 'Two's A Crowd' , Masgard in 'The Living Dead', Major Peter Rooke in 'Split' and went on to become a Bond villain in the 1981 movie *For Your Eyes Only*?

#57 - Cars

1 Mike Gambit drove what car?

2 From the Keel era to the early Cathy Gale episodes, which car did Steed claim to drive?

3 How many Rolls Royces did Steed have in the series?

4 What is the colour of Emma Peel's first Lotus?

5 What was Steed's first car in the Tara King era?

6 In *The New Avengers*, what is the car that Steed uses while in Canada?

7 What kind of transmission are Steed's yellow Rover and green Jaguar in *The New Avengers*?

8 Which member of the production team had their actual car used for the car chase where Mike Gambit follows the van that has kidnapped Von Claus in 'The Eagle's Nest'?

9 What make of car is John Steed famous for driving?

10 What model of Lotus did Tara King drive?

11 How many cars did Steed drive in *The New Avengers* and what were they?

12 What car is Purdey forced to drive in 'Sleeper'?

Points Available: **12**
Your current score: ____

#58 - Episodic Trivia - The New Avengers – Part A

1   The Eagle's Nest

1   What is the tune whistled by Steed, Purdey and Gambit as they escort the criminals away?

2   What country formed the setting?

3   From where did Purdey say that Steed had obtained strong wrists?

4   Who were the monks trying to resurrect?

5   How did Steed communicate with Gambit while he was on the island of St Dorca?

6   What gun does Gambit use?

7   What establishment was Purdey thrown out of for being too tall?

2   The Midas Touch

1   What commodity does Professor Turner like to deal in?

2   What are Gambit and Purdey eating during the car chase?

3   Who does Steed barely recognise when they come off the plane because they've put on a lot of weight?

4   What animal is Professor Turner hunting while he is being watched by Freddy?

5   What career did Gambit miss a chance at?

3 HOUSE OF CARDS

1 Who is sent a playing card to kill Gambit?

2 What was the name of the friend whom Steed cradled as they died?

3 Who was the villain?

4 What did Steed's date try to poison him with?

5 How did Ivan Perov trail Steed's car?

6 How did Steed describe Ivan Perov?

7 What suit is missing from the deck of cards?

8 What does Steed put onto Olga's eye after his punch to her face?

4 LAST OF THE CYBERNAUTS???

1 What is the name of Professor Mason's machine?

2 What game is Steed playing when he attacks fellow agent Tom Fitzroy?

3 What is the name of Steed's housekeeper?

4 Where is Felix Kane ambushed?

5 What spray defeats Felix Kane?

6 Who reported to Steed about Felix Kane?

5 TO CATCH A RAT

1 What code-name was used by Steed to save his life going over the wall and ended with a group of nudists being attacked on a private coach?

2 What was the code-name for Irwin Gunner?

3 What traitor was Irwin Gunner looking for?

4 Where was Irwin Gunner based?

5 What is site C?

6 CAT AMONGST THE PIGEONS

1 Who was the villain?

2 What do Steed and Gambit use to rescue Purdey from a bird attack?

3 What instrument controlled the birds?

4 Where do Steed and Professor Waterlow hide from the bird attack?

5 What causes Turner's death?

6 What was the name of Zarcardi's home?

7 Who warned Steed about Rydercroft?

11 SLEEPER

1 What is the name of the gas used by the bank robbers?

2 What does Mike Gambit get every year from his aunt?

3 How did the villains get around the city?

4 What item did Mike Gambit describe as his 'Small volume of hints for a growing boy'?

5 How many children did Steed say an uncle of his sired?

12 GNAWS

1 What creature is accidentally created by Charles Thornton?

2 Who is the Russian agent searching the sewers?

3 What alerted Steed to the problems going on in the sewers?

4 What were the two big clues as to the identity of the villain?

5 What vegetable grew to large proportions in a locker?

13 DIRTIER BY THE DOZEN

1 What is the title of the unit causing wars for private gain?

2 What rank is held by Gambit when he infiltrates the unit?

3 Where does Purdey end up stranded?

4 What is Colonel Miller's nickname?

5 How is Purdey rescued?

Points Available: **77**

Your current score: ____

#59 - Who's Who? - Part 3

1 Which actor played Gilbert in 'The Fear Merchants' and Sexton in 'Take Over', but found fame as Frank Haskins in The Sweeney?

2 Which Not The Nine O'Clock News star and Mrs Billy Connolly appeared in The New Avengers episode 'Angels of Death'?

3 Which Duty Free star played Draker in The New Avengers episode 'Target'?

4 Which Bergerac star appeared in The Avengers episodes 'The Town of No Return', 'The Correct Way to Kill', 'Love All' and The New Avengers episode 'Angels of Death'?

5 Which actor famous for his loud voice appeared in the episodes 'The Superlative Seven' and 'The Morning After'?

6 Which actress played Mrs Hana Wild in the episode 'The Superlative Seven'?

7 Which actor played John Cartney in 'A Touch of Brimstone' and Stewart Kirby in 'Epic'?

8 Which actor played Varnals in 'Room Without A View', Max Prendergast in 'The Joker' and Ivan Perov in 'House of Cards'?

9 Which Welsh actor appeared in the episodes 'Six Hands Across A Table', 'Death of a Batman', 'The Correct Way to Kill' and 'My Wildest Dream'?

10 Which star of Only Fools and Horses appeared in The New Avengers episode 'Dirtier By the Dozen'?

Points Available: **10**
Your current score: _____

#60 - Behind The Scenes - Series 6

1 In what episode did Linda Thorson begin using her own hair rather than having to bother with a wig?

    A) Split!   *B) All Done*   *C) The*
                        With Mirrors   *Interrogators*

2 Patrick Macnee injured what part of his body while filming a scene in 'Love All'?

    A) His neck   *B) His ribs*   *C) His bowler hat*

3 What was the first episode directed by Ray Austin?

    A) Have Guns –   *B) Have Flight –*   *C) Have TV –*
      Will Haggle   *Will Travel*   *Will Watch*

4 What is Linda Thorson first seen to be wearing when she catches the flowers in the Series 6 opening?

    A) Black leather   *B) A black dress*   *C) A black robe*

5 Who directed the last episode of *The Avengers*?

    A) Leslie Norman   *B) Barry Norman*   *C) Norman Price*

6 Which episode featured the moving target opening titles filmed for the USA?

    A) Thingumajig   *B) Fog*   *C) Split!*

Points Available: 6
Your current score: ____

#61 - Episodic Trivia - The New Avengers - Part B

14 Hostage

1 Who is the actor who played Spelman and went on to star as John Steed in the stage play?

2 Who was the villain responsible for Purdey's kidnap in a plan to discredit Steed's department?

3 What warning did Steed give to Gambit?

4 Which villain annoyingly called Purdey 'Sweetheart'?

5 What is the name of Steed's girlfriend who is jealous of Purdey?

6 How much money was Purdey's ransom?

7 What did Steed find under the back seat of his car?

15 Trap

1 What was the name of the villain?

2 What was Steed's injury following the plane crash?

3 Who was the CIA agent teaming up with Steed, Purdey and Gambit?

4 To which famous figure was the street cleaner compared?

5 What did Gambit find for luck as he made makeshift weapons?

16 DEAD MEN ARE DANGEROUS

1 Where did Mark Crayford plan his final showdown with Steed?

2 What item did Mark Crayford use to cheat in his only win over Steed?

3 What is the name of the file keeper?

4 What year was John Steed placed on the honours board of the cricket club?

5 What happens to Steed's Bentley?

6 What is Steed's motto regarding women?

17 MEDIUM RARE

1 What is the name of Steed's friend who is killed?

2 Who runs the string of informants?

3 Who insists to Purdey that Steed is a traitor?

4 What is the name of the medium who visits Steed and warns him of danger?

5 What show did Steed end up going to in a planned setup – even though he dislikes it?

18 ANGELS OF DEATH

1 Where was Manderson when he was stressed to his death?

2 What type of picture puzzle caused stress-induced death?

3 Who was the traitor behind the Briantern Health Farm?

4 What game is Purdey playing with a daisy as she waits with Steed at the border?

5 What machine is Purdey placed into when she is discovered?

19 OBSESSION

1 Which of Steed's cars was used to deflect the missile?

2 How did Steed protect Purdey when she was accused of being a traitor?

3 Whose death is provoking Larry Doomer's obsession?

4 In what location was Purdey and Larry's dream home to be?

5 Who are Larry Doomer's helpers?

20 THE LION AND THE UNICORN

1 What rating is held by The Unicorn?

2 What part of the building did Steed use to secure the release of a hostage from The Unicorn's men?

3 What impressed The Unicorn when he was captured by Steed, Purdey and Gambit?

4 In which country did Steed, Purdey and Gambit catch top assassin The Unicorn?

5 In what sport was Purdey part of the ladies team at the Sorbonne?

6 Where did Steed almost succeed in killing The Unicorn?

7 How does The Unicorn die?

21 K IS FOR KILL – PART ONE

1 What is the name of the Ambassador who seeks Steed's help?

2 How did Steed describe the difference between beer and wine?

3 What does Gambit say that Steed needs to replenish?

4 What letter does Purdey state as she plays 'I Spy' in Steed's car?

5 What kind of grenade does Steed recognise when it lands near him?

22 K Is For Kill – Part Two

1 What alerts Gambit to the location of the assassin?

2 What saves Steed's life from a bullet?

3 What is the occasion that draws out the target for the K agent?

4 Who the Colonel in charge of the resurrection plan?

5 What award is Purdey given?

23 Complex

1 What is the name of the assassin everyone is trying to find?

2 Who is the Canadian contact who is assassinated as he tries to pass on information to Steed?

3 Where in England do Steed, Purdey and Gambit meet their contact for details about the assassin?

4 What is the code of the assassin?

5 What element defeats Scapina?

24 The Gladiators

1 What kind of holiday are Steed, Gambit and Purdey taking?

2 Who does Karl Sminsky work for?

3 Where did Karl Sminsky go to perfect his lethal training?

4 What is the name of the man whom Gambit recognises?

5 Where are Sminsky and his agents breaking into?

6 What did Steed add to the equation to defeat Karl Sminsky's training method towards projectiles?

25 FORWARD BASE

1 What was the name of the typhoon that was used as cover for the enemy agents?

2 What did Steed use to discover the location of Forward Base?

3 What is the name of the agent who meets up with Steed?

4 What is thrown into the lake?

5 What animal do the boats resemble?

6 Who is the enemy agent who Purdey and Gambit recognise?

26 EMILY

1 The name of what animal is the traitor Steed is pursuing?

2 What is the hobby of Miss Daly that is only revealed after the success of the mission?

3 What first covered the hand print on the roof of the car?

4 How does Steed plug up the holes in Emily's radiator?

5 What hats are used on the car?

6 What shrinks Purdey's jumper?

Points Available: **73**
Your current score: _____

#62 - Quick Test - The New Avengers

1 In *The New Avengers* episode 'Dirtier By The Dozen', Ballard Berkley played Purdey's uncle Elroy, but which sitcom was he best known for being in?

    A) As Time Goes By   *B) The Good Life*   *C) Fawlty Towers*

2 Mike Gambit was arrested and put into jail in which episode?

    A) Complex   *B) Hostage*   *C) Trap*

3 Purdey was shot in the arm in which episode?

    A) Obsession   *B) Gnaws*   *C) Complex*

4 In whish episode did the song 'Colonel Bogey' appear?

    A) The Eagle's Nest   *B) The Midas Touch*   *C) The Lion and The Unicorn*

5 What character name is mentioned in '*Medium Rare*' only to appear as a central character in the later ITC series *The Professionals*, played by Gordon Jackson?

    A) George Horsely   *B) George Sheeply*   *C) George Cowley*

6 What are the colours of *The New Avengers* logo?

    A) Yellow and Green   *B) Black and Blue*   *C) Red, White and Blue*

7 What was Purdey before she became a department agent?

    A) Gourmet Chef   *B) Ballerina*   *C) Fighter Pilot*

8 On what date does Steed hold his annual parties where there is nothing to drink but champagne?

    A) June 13th   *B) December 25th*   *C) July 4th*

#63 - Who's Who? - Part 4

1 Which actress who played Pussy
   Cat in 'Dressed to Kill' was also
   Doctor Who companion Polly
   Wright and was once married to
   actor Michael Gough?

2 Which *To The Manor Born* star
   played four villains over the
   course of the series: Neil
   Anstice in 'Second Sight', John
   Harvey in 'Dial A Deadly
   Number', Waldo Thyssen in
   'Escape in Time' and Ezdorf in
   'Get-A-Way'?

3 Which star of sitcom *Porridge*
   played Professor Chadwick in
   'Return of the Cybernauts' and
   The Master in 'Bizarre'?

4 Which actor, well known for a
   lemonade commercial, played
   Peter Omrod in 'Silent Dust',
   Brinstead in 'Killer' and later
   Tommy McKay in *The New
   Avengers* episode 'Hostage'?

5 Which Scottish actor, famous for playing Fraser in *Dad's Army*, appeared in '*Death of a Great Dane*', '*Brief For Murder*', '*A Funny Thing Happened on the Way To The Station*' and '*Pandora*'?

6 In '*Propellant 23*', who was the actor playing the Flight Captain who went on to become the Brigadier in *Doctor Who*?

7 Which *Last of the Summer Wine* actor played Hal Anderson in '*The Wringer*'?

8 In the episode '*Esprit de Corps*' which famous actor from *The Sweeney* and *Inspector Morse* played the role of Captain Trench?

9 Which actor played Frank Compton in '*Split!*' and the doctor working for Murder International in '*Requiem*', but was noted for playing Superintendent Jack McVitie in the Scottish police series *Taggart*?

10 Who played Baron Von Curt in '*They Keep Killing Steed*' and went on to play Simon Templar in *Return of The Saint*?

Points Available: **10**
Your current score: _____

#64 - CROSSWORD 4

Across

1 Episode title; staying awake is difficult. (7)

4 His touch means death. (5)

5 The way to have a steak but an unusual visitor to Steed's home. (4)

6 Episode title; must be dead on. (6)

9 Steed and Purdey's partner. (10)

10 Heavenly gifts resulting in death. (6)

Down

2 Surname of Purdey actress. (6)

3 Special drink invented by Purdey in *Dead Men Are Dangerous*. (6)

7 Episode title; giant rat. (5)

8 Something red that appeared on clothes after a visit to the target range. (3)

Points Available: **10**

Anagram answer: _____ (1 extra point)

Your current score: ____

#65 - Conundrum 5

Above everything, this person is absolutely fabulous;

YOJANA MULLEN

Who is it?

_ _ _ _ _ _   _ _ _ _ _ _

Points Available: **1**
Your current score: ____

#66 – Dial Some Friendly Numbers

1 Counting *The New Avengers*, how many episodes of *The Avengers* are there ?

2 How many episodes of *The Avengers* featured Linda Thorson?

3 Who is trainee agent 69?

4 How many times did TaraKing drive Steed's Rolls Royce?

5 In how many episodes did Mother appear?

6 How many times did Steed get 100% on the target range in *The New Avengers* episode '*Target!*'?

7 After how many years was the lost episode '*Tunnel of Fear*' discovered?

8 Julie Stevens played Venus Smith in how many episodes?

9 Whose telephone code is Sloane 0181?

10 How many episodes featured Dr Martin King?

Points Available: **10**
Your current score: _____

#67 - The Stage Play

1 Which famous *Carry On...* film star directed *The Avengers* stage play?

2 Which actor who appeared in *The Avengers* episodes 'You Have Just Been Murdered' and 'Super Secret Cypher Snatch' played John Steed?

3 Which actress who appeared in the episode 'A Surfeit of H2O' played Steed's partner, Mrs Hannah Wild?

4 Who was the actress who appeared in the episode 'Stay Tuned' and played the villain of the stage play?

5 What domestic servant did Steed have in the stage play who did not appear in the series and is usually associated with Bruce Wayne?

6 At which theatres was the stage play performed?

7 Who worked with Brian Clemens to write the stage play following on from an Avengers connection in which he was the writer of the episodes 'Nightmare' and *The New Avengers* episode 'To Catch a Rat'?

8 What was the name of the main villain in the stage play?

9 Hannah Wild was originally a character ho featured in which Series 5 episode?

10 Did the stage play have a long run?

Points Available: **10**
Your current score: _____

#68 - Clothes Maketh The Avenger

B	O	N	O	I	T	A	N	R	A	C	B	A	B	H
A	O	Q	A	D	G	S	G	O	B	S	R	F	D	A
D	S	W	Q	A	B	D	A	V	C	L	I	T	T	B
S	V	E	L	E	A	T	H	E	R	W	C	I	E	A
G	J	T	A	E	K	P	I	I	D	U	K	W	U	S
J	E	U	M	B	R	E	L	L	A	I	I	K	D	R
K	T	R	I	F	M	H	T	S	N	P	N	L	G	E
L	L	Y	S	L	B	H	A	K	L	O	H	M	J	L
M	I	I	D	A	X	N	Y	T	M	L	A	A	L	E
C	H	P	P	R	A	B	E	A	N	C	N	N	P	E
N	S	O	A	G	O	K	S	Y	O	S	D	C	U	P
V	F	L	T	O	Q	E	F	P	A	Y	B	O	T	A
I	A	N	T	H	E	S	T	E	R	T	A	N	P	M
C	R	S	E	G	H	T	O	N	M	B	G	P	X	M
N	U	G	R	E	T	R	A	G	S	M	X	J	U	E

CARNATION
EMMAPEELERS
GARTER GUN
BRICK IN HANDBAG
BOWLER HAT
LEATHER
KINKY BOOTS
UMBRELLA

Points Available: **8**
Your current score: _____

#69 – LOCATION, LOCATION, LOCATION

1 What is the name of the town where Emma Peel tells Steed to meet her after he's sorted out the children consisting of Gordon, Albert, Julian and little baby Brian?

2 Where in the world was the home of Mrs Catherine Gale before her husband was killed on their farm?

3 Which location was used to film *The Avengers* from Series 4 onwards and was also home to several ITC shows including *The Saint*?

4 In what part of London were the headquarters of SNOB?

5 Where is the unit located in '*The Wringer*'?

6 Which member of the production team used their home as a location in '*Noon Doomsday*'?

7 Where in Hertfordshire is '*Murdersville*'?

8 What are the locations in *The Avengers* affectionately termed as?

9 What is the location of the house to which Emma Peel is lured in '*The Joker*'?

10 Where does Steed say he has returned from holiday in '*The Charmers*'?

Points Available: **10**

Your current score: ____

#70 - Big Finish

1 Emily Woodward plays Tara King; but who is her father who was made famous playing the titular role in *Callan* and Robert McCall in *The Equalizer*?

2 Which actor took on the role of Mother after originally appearing in the TV series as J.J. Hooter in '*How to Succeed... At Murder*' and as the driver in '*Never, Never Say Die*'?

3 Which actor voices John Steed?

4 Which set of *The Avengers* audio was specially dedicated to Patrick Macnee following his passing in 2015?

5 Linda Thorson guest starred in which audio story?

6 Which 1991 novel written by Dave Rogers and John Peel was adapted by Big Finish?

7 How many volumes are there of *The Avengers: The Lost Episodes*?

8 What is the connection that links TV series producer Brian Clemens and Big Finish audio director Sam Clemens?

9 Which actress voices Emma Peel?

10 Which actor voices Dr David Keel?

11 What was Paul O'Grady's character name in the story where he guest starred in *The Comic Strip Adaptations* Volume 7?

Points Available: **10**
Your current score: _____

#71 – Under The Hat 9 – The New Avengers

1 Joanna Lumley was born in India – true or false?

2 Gareth Hunt also appeared in *Upstairs Downstairs* – true or false?

3 Joanna Lumley was once married to Jeremy Lloyd, co-creator of sitcoms *'Allo, 'Allo* and *Are You Being Served?* – true or false?

4 Joanna Lumley is a dame – true or false?

5 Gareth Hunt was privately a good guitarist – true or false?

6 Brian Clemens sketched and designed the opening titles to *The New Avengers* – true or false?

7 There were two title sequences to *The New Avengers* – true or false?

Points Available: 7
Your current score: ____

#72 - Conundrum 6

Began as Steed's medical man before reaching the big screen;

RYAN HEIND

Who is it?

___ _____

#73 - Avengers Sudoku 3

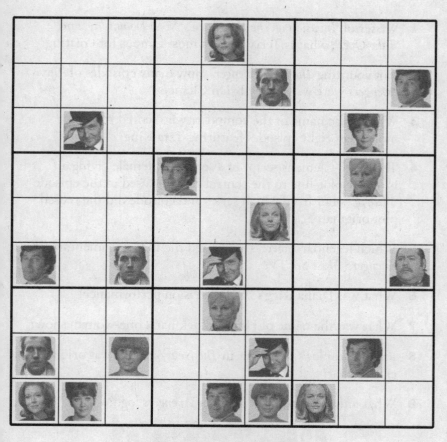

Complete the picture pattern using the key below.

S = Steed

K = David Keel

C = Cathy Gale

E = Emma Peel

T = Tara King

P = Purdey

G = Mike Gambit

M = Mother

R = Rhonda

Points Available: 10

Your current score: ____

#74 - The Big Thinker

1 Writer of *'Invasion of The Earthmen'*, *'Noon Doomsday'* and *'Take-Over'*; what is Terry Nation most famous for creating?

2 Not counting *The New Avengers*, how many episodes of *The Avengers* were written by Brian Clemens?

3 What is the name of the composer who scored music for more than eight episodes featuring Tara King?

4 The Brian Clemens script of a semi-clad female giving an intrinsic plot-line to the central cast was used in the episode *'Bizarre'* – but from which series and episode did the reused plot originate?

5 Which legendary actress presented the ITV documentary *The Avengers: Must See TV*?

6 What was Diana Rigg's final television performance?

7 What was the name of Honor Blackman's one-woman show?

8 Joanna Lumley's character in *The New Avengers* was originally called what?

9 What animal features in *The New Avengers* logo?

Points Available: **9**
Your current score: ____

#75 - Conundrum 7

This person was both upstairs and downstairs before becoming an Avenger, but they had a good hand for coffee;

REG H T THAUN

Who is it?

‒ ‒ ‒ ‒ ‒ ‒   ‒ ‒ ‒ ‒

#76 - Crossword 5

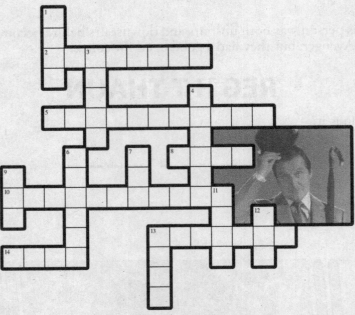

Across

2 Steed always had this rainy day item (8)

5 Episode title; plot deals with a deadly little black box (11)

8 Patrick Macnee novel; *Dead ...?* (4)

10 Name given to Diana Rigg's series 5 catsuits (11)

13 Episode title; plot involves a wrestling Balkan president (7)

14 Episode title; *The Grandeur That Was ...?* (4)

Down

1 Affectionate term for Steed's house in *The New Avengers*; Steed's ...? (4)

3 Name of enemy agent Kartovski (5)

4 Make of Steed and Gambit's cars in *The New Avengers* (6)

6 Place for horses and Steed's address from Series 5 onward (6)

7 Number before Steed's bosses Ten and Twelve (3)

9 Not the old Avengers (3)

11 Episode where Steed loses three weeks and meets Father; *... Tuned?* (4)

12 Episode title; plot deals with The Gaslight Ghoul of 1888 (3)

13 Author and aficionado on *The Avengers*; Mr Rogers (4)

Points Available: **10**
Your current score: ____

SCORE SHEET

Out of a possible 1,518 points - let us see how well you have scored for the department;

- **< 50:** You have become a courier of top secret information - pass it on and return home.

- **< 100:** You will be considered to undertake proper secret agent training

- **< 300:** Your potential is recognised - you are the new Agent 69!

- **< 500:** You have been taught the Steed methods but need further training.

- **< 600:** You are seriously being considered for active duty in the field.

- **< 800:** Reports of your potential are spreading through the department.

- **< 900:** You are the star pupil in training and pass your course with flying colours.

- **< 1,250:** You are ready to meet the legendary John Steed.

- **< 1,500:** You will be assigned a partner and be considered for some very important department work.

- **1,500+:** You are a top secret agent within the department and have earned your bowler hat and umbrella!

Congratulations!

No matter what your score - welcome into one of the most vital British government departments that serves the world.

From here you can use your knowledge amongst your community, recognise fellow agents and assist in the wonders that come thick and fast in the world of fandom.

Your knowledge is a vital asset - protect yourself at all times. Keep the bowler on whenever there is stress and deal with the endless number of diabolical masterminds.

Champagne is in order!

But you have instructions awaiting you; proceed to 3 Stable Mews, Westminster in the city of London where you will meet your contact.

Good luck, agent of fandom!

THE
ANSWERS

1 MRS EMMA PEEL

1. Fighter Pilot.   2. That Steed likes his tea stirred anti-clockwise.
3. Knight.   4. In the Amazon jungle.   5. *'Death At Bargain Prices'*.
6. Knight Industries.   7. *'A Touch of Brimstone'*.   8. Elma Peem.
9. Auburn.   10. Eleanor Bron.   11. A large eye.   13. Herself.   14. A
diamond tie pin.   15. Amateur.

2 CROSSWORD 1

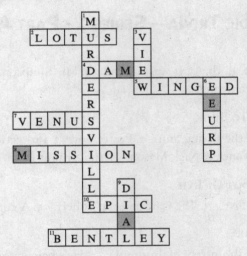

Hidden name: *Emma*

3 CONUNDRUM 1

Patrick Macnee

4 UNDER THE HAT 1 - DEPARTMENT TRIVIA

1. True; his middle name was Patrick. 2. False. 3. True. 4. False; Paul O'Grady was a massive Avengers fan. He performed a two-part sketch in his Lily Savage persona with Simon Williams as Steed. He presented *The Avengers 50th Anniversary* celebrations in Chichester in 2011 and also had a dream come true playing Septimus Crump in *The Avengers* Big Finish audio story '*This Train Terminates Here*' before his passing. 5. True.

5 EPISODIC TRIVIA – SERIES 1 - PART A

1. **HOT SNOW**

   1. Spicer. 2. Both. 3. It was raining. 4. Mrs Simpson.
   5. Engagement rings.

2. **BROUGHT TO BOOK**

   1. House of the Rising Sun. 2. Pretty Boy. 3. Protection rackets.
   4. Ronnie Vance & Nick Mason. 5. In a peanut bowl.

3. **SQUARE ROOT OF EVIL**

   1. Irish. 2. Five. 3. The Cardinal. 4. Tobert. 5. A cut hand.

4. **NIGHTMARE**

   1. Professor Braintree. 2. Insomnia. 3. He's being attacked by lab rats. 4. Dr Jones. 5. Canasta.

5. **CRESCENT MOON**

   1. Carmelite. 2. Pascala. 3. His youth. 4. Vasco. 5. The 'late' General Mendoza.

6. **GIRL ON THE TRAPEZE**

   1. Danilov. 2. The Circus. 3. A cigarette. 4. A powder. 5. Zibbo.
   6. West 2. 7. Vera, the high diver. 8. Radeck. 9. Trapeze artist.
   10. "Here we go again."

7. **DIAMOND CUT DIAMOND**

   1. Airline Pilot.   2. Smuggling.   3. Hit and run.   4. He is framed for murder.   5. Stella Creighton.

8. **THE RADIOACTIVE MAN**

   1. Marko Ogrin.   2. His wife is having a baby.   3. A radioactive pellet.   4. Peter.   5. A Geiger counter.

9. **ASHES OF ROSES**

   1. Olive and Jacques Berrone.   2. Arson and Insurance fraud. 3. A faulty hairdryer.   4. Johnny Mendellsohn.   5. To walk the dog.

10. **HUNT THE MAN DOWN**

    1. Frank Preston.   2. Rocky and Stacey.   3. £100,000.   4. Carol. 5. Sewers.

11. **PLEASE, DON'T FEED THE ANIMALS**

    1. A Monkey.   2. General.   3. Crocodile.   4. Felgate; a civil servant. 5. A fist fight.

12. **DANCE WITH DEATH**

    1. Elaine Bateman.   2. His scarf.   3. It's been redecorated.   4. CN; the Change of Name catalogue.   5. A diamond necklace.

13. **ONE FOR THE MORTUARY**

    1. On an invitation card.   2. A Turkish bath.   3. He has one eye. 4. Taxidermist.   5. Don't lose touch.

6   SERIES 1 - QUICK TEST

   1. A) 'Hot Snow'.   2. B) 'Brought To Book'.   3. B) 'Diamond Cut Diamond'.

7 WORD SEARCH 1 - DRINK, MRS PEEL?

C	H	A	M	P	O	I	C	A	W	G	T	Y	U	B
T	E	D	O	C	H	A	M	P	A	G	N	E	N	Y
S	J	P	A	X	T	E	R	J	A	E	B	A	S	R
A	B	A	S	V	Z	T	N	A	H	K	L	X	E	F
V	S	T	E	A	V	Q	Y	B	M	X	G	N	G	H
E	F	A	C	O	C	H	A	M	P	A	G	N	E	A
N	N	R	A	A	X	H	Y	O	Z	A	P	Q	E	Z
C	A	A	T	N	O	T	A	E	P	E	A	J	V	X
H	A	P	H	Q	R	W	A	M	B	H	X	V	N	Q
A	C	D	Y	A	N	K	A	M	P	L	I	E	P	U
M	B	C	Y	M	J	H	X	A	C	A	C	B	U	I
P	V	M	W	M	C	T	G	H	X	L	G	P	R	Y
A	Z	H	H	E	D	A	H	B	A	E	Y	N	D	T
G	B	C	Y	E	S	E	C	Z	A	V	T	Q	E	O
N	N	H	Q	X	A	V	E	B	S	T	K	L	Y	E
E	D	B	A	K	V	A	L	O	H	C	M	V	N	F
D	E	T	S	B	N	E	N	G	A	P	M	A	H	C

8 CONUNDRUM 2

Diana Rigg

9 UNDER THE HAT 2 - DEPARTMENT TRIVIA

1. True; he played Invisible Jones, the department archivist.
2. True. 3. True; Honor Blackman in *Goldfinger* (1964), Diana Rigg and Joanna Lumley in *On Her Majesty's Secret Service* (1969) and Patrick Macnee in *A View To A Kill* (1985). 4. True; Sydney Newman was a Canadian producer who was involved with both *Doctor Who* and *The Avengers*. 5. True; he began as a stunt man on the show from the colour Diana Rigg series and went on to directing. 6. False; the first series episodes 'Hot Snow' and 'Brought To Book' are considered a two-parter. *The New Avengers* two parter was *K is For Kill*.

10 Episodic Trivia – Series 1 - Part B

14. The Springers
1. Prison.   2. Dr Fenton.   3. A young girls' finishing school.
4. Caroline.   5. Commander Kenilworthy.

15. The Frighteners
1. Witch-hazel.   2. Moxon.   3. Fred.   4. A massage contract.   5. His blood pressure.   6. Italian.   7. Inspector Foster.   8. Mrs Briggs; but actually Doris Courtney, a friend of David Keel's.   9. A shave.
10. Through a window.

16. The Yellow Needle
1. Diabetes.   2. James Sanderson, a journalist.   3. Kondor.
4. Medicine.   5. Jacquetta Brown, Sir Wilberforce's secretary.

17. Death On The Slipway
1. A dockyard.   2. Kolchek.   3. Metallurgist.   4. Fleming.
5. A bomb.

18. Double Danger
1. Steed.   2. Diamonds.   3. Palmers Drive.   4. Bruton.
5. John Bartholomew.

19. Toy Trap
1. Bunty Seton.   2. A vice ring.   3. Bussell's.   4. In a toy wigwam.
5. Mrs McCabe.

20. Tunnel Of Fear
1. Harry Black.   2. Estate agent.   3. His dog, Puppy.   4. Rolls Royce.
5. Fairground barker.   6. An explosive cigarette.   7. Four.   8. They reconstructed the crime.   9. Delta.   10. Southend-on-Sea.

21. The Far Distant Dead
1. A cyclone.   2. Mexico.   3. Hydraulic fluid.   4. Hercule Zeebrugge.   5. Rayner.

22. KILL THE KING

1. On the plane bringing him to London. 2. Major Harrington.
3. Creighton-Bull. 4. By a helicopter. 5. U-Meng.

23. DEAD OF WINTER

1. Hans Gerhardt Schneider. 2. Inez. 3. Phoenix. 4. Harry.
5. Willie.

24. THE DEADLY AIR

1. Truscott Research Laboratory. 2. A vaccine. 3. A guinea pig.
4. Professor Kilbride. 5. Dr Owen Craxton.

25. A CHANGE OF BAIT

1. Bananas. 2. He is her landlord. 3. A heart attack. 4. In a
Victorian wardrobe. 5. Barker.

26. DRAGONSFIELD

1. Radiation hazards in space. 2. One-Fifteen. 3. Lisa Strauss.
4. Saunders. 5. Susan Summers.

11 BEHIND THE SCENES – SERIES 1

1. C) *Police Surgeon*. 2. B) John Dankworth. 3. B) *Brought To Book*.
4. C) 1984. 5. A) Leonard White. 6. A) Don Leaver.
7. C) Barbara Wodehouse. 8. B) *'Please, Don't Feed The Animals'*.
9. C) Robert Fuest.

12 DR DAVID KEEL

1. G.P. 2. *'The Frighteners'*. 3. WHO; World Health Organisation.
4. Dr Richard Tredding. 5. Getting married. 6. Peggy. 7. *'Toy
Trap'*. 8. Scotch. 9. He was a locum at her father's practice.
10. Sir Wilberforce Lungi.

13 WORD SEARCH 2 - HAVE A WORD!

E	N	D	O	P	T	L	A	K	C	O	L	R	A	W
R	O	L	E	V	J	S	B	R	O	T	L	K	X	D
R	H	E	A	H	J	B	D	K	O	C	M	A	V	E
A	J	I	G	I	K	I	L	D	A	D	E	M	P	A
Z	K	F	S	H	N	P	K	P	D	M	N	B	C	Z
I	R	S	P	L	I	T	P	E	C	Q	B	A	L	X
B	C	N	A	B	A	C	E	G	W	P	C	I	P	E
B	N	O	F	A	V	T	Q	R	V	Y	M	A	B	R
U	X	G	N	A	S	B	Y	O	C	X	P	G	H	A
L	Q	A	K	C	V	G	E	K	A	R	D	N	A	M
L	K	R	N	S	E	G	W	D	K	P	I	L	R	T
S	L	D	X	C	B	R	A	D	M	W	J	M	K	H
E	P	A	D	H	A	M	T	H	A	E	V	S	E	G
Y	H	M	G	H	I	K	D	O	A	H	J	S	N	I
E	T	H	I	N	G	U	M	A	J	I	G	B	A	N

14 UNDER THE HAT 3 - SERIES 1

1. False; it was Ray Rigby.   2. False; he was married 3 times.
3. True.   4. False; he appeared in all episodes apart from two in series 1.   5. True; she played Peggy in '*Hot Snow*' and Laure in '*Propellant 23*'

15 CROSSWORD 2

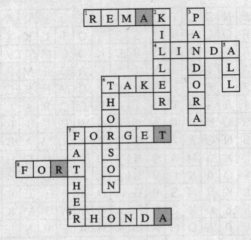

Hidden name: *Tara*

16 EPISODIC TRIVIA - SERIES 2 – PART A

1. **DEAD ON COURSE**

   1. Vincent O'Brien.   2. Ireland.   3. A Molotov Cocktail.   4. By reading the phone dial in Freidman's office.   5. He was strangled.

2. **MISSION TO MONTREAL**

   1. Carla Berotti.   2. District Early Warning line.   3. On a ship.
   4. Steward.   5. Sheila Dowson.

3. **THE SELL OUT**

   1. One-Twelve.   2. Barber.   3. Mark Harvey.   4. The British Museum.   5. With a rugby tackle.

4. **DEATH DISPATCH**

   1. Jamaica.   2. Miguel Rosas.   3. A toy doll.   4. Champagne.
   5. Holding his daughter hostage.

5. **WARLOCK**

   1. The Natural History Museum. 2. Cosmo Gallion. 3. Midnight.
   4. Black. 5. Mrs Dunning.

6. **PROPELLANT 23**

   1. Meyer. 2. Curly. 3. Fruit Juice. 4. Jacques. 5. In her garter.

7. **MR TEDDY BEAR**

   1. Cyanide. 2. £100,000 per killing. 3. Nerve gas with a blistering
   agent. 4. An adult chimpanzee. 5. Diamonds.

8. **THE DECAPOD**

   1. Yakob Borb. 2. Wrestling. 3. Wrestling ring. 4. The Balkan
   Embassy. 5. Harry Ramsden.

9. **BULLSEYE**

   1. Anderson's. 2. Vulgar. 3. Brigadier. 4. Carl. 5. Her broker.

10. **THE REMOVAL MEN**

    1. Her aunt's house in Nice. 2. His wife's necklace. 3. Killed in his
    cell. 4. Sing For Your Supper. 5. Les Centaurs.

11. **THE MAURITIUS PENNY**

    1. He was shot. 2. The dentist. 3. A collectible book of stamps.
    4. His shoes. 5. Elsie.

12. **DEATH OF A GREAT DANE**

    1. Getz. 2. A human body. 3. In the stomach. 4. Alexander Litoff.
    5. Two.

13. **DEATH ON THE ROCKS**

    1. Rock Salt. 2. Hatton Garden. 3. That they be married. 4. Liza
    Denham. 5. Max Daniels.

17 SERIES 2 - QUICK TEST PART 1

   1. B) 'The Removal Men'. 2. A) 'Mr Teddy Bear'. 3. A) 'Propellant 23'.
   4. C) 'Immortal Clay'. 5. A) A Crustacean.

18 Under The Hat 4 - Series 2

1. True; stories from Honor Blackman tell of him 'Winging it like mad!'. 2. False; Honor Blackman had no stunt double. 3. True. 4. False; Kenny Ball was, however, a frequent guest of Morecambe and Wise. 5. False; the first choice was Nyree Dawn Porter.

19 Episodic Trivia - Series 2 – Part B

14. Traitor In Zebra

1. Pink Gin. 2. Nicotine. 3. A note in the collar of his dog. 4. Through the dart board. 5. Locks him in the room with his own bomb.

15. The Big Thinker

1. Plato. 2. Gambling. 3. Electrocuted in the air vent. 4. Pinball. 5. Carruthers.

16. Intercrime

1. Hilda Stern. 2. W. Felder. 3. Defence Council. 4. One of the prison guards. 5. Pamela Johnson.

17. Immortal Clay

1. A cup. 2. In a Turkish bath. 3. Blomberg. 4. His glove found at the scene of the murder. 5. In the slip tank.

18. Box Of Tricks

1. A faith healer. 2. "Got that? Got that?". 3. The General's massuese. 4. A tape recorder. 5. Gerry Weston, the magician.

19. The Golden Eggs

1. Galileo. 2. Clockwork. 3. Brushing his teeth. 4. His 'Ice cold' hotel. 5. Virus Verity Prime.

20. School For Traitors

1. One-Seven. 2. Jack Roberts. 3. Professor Shanklin. 4. Dr Johnson. 5. Artist.

21. THE WHITE DWARF

1. Barker. 2. Tor Point. 3. The sun. 4. Sheba. 5. Professor Cartwright.

22. MAN IN THE MIRROR

1. Taking his picture in the funhouse mirror. 2. Betty. 3. 24 Hours. 4. Strong. 5. The Ghost Tunnel.

23. CONSPIRACY OF SILENCE

1. Omerta. 2. London, Montreal and New York. 3. Walking his dog. 4. Leggo. 5. Sica.

24. A CHORUS OF FROGS

1. The Frogs. 2. A yacht. 3. Archipelago Mason. 4. 100 fathoms. 5. In Venus Smith's cabin.

25. SIX HANDS ACROSS A TABLE

1. Oliver Waldner. 2. Through the window. 3. Rosalind. 4. Twice. 5. Sir Charles Reniston.

26. KILLER WHALE

1. Ambergris. 2. Fernand. 3. For one month. 4. Joey Frazer. 5. Sailor.

20 SERIES 2 - QUICK TEST PART 2

1. B) Carlo. 2. A) Martin. 3. B) Singer. 4. A) Trap him with it.

21 BEHIND THE SCENES – SERIES 2

1. A) Judy. 2. C) Leather. 3. A) Callan.

22 CONUNDRUM 3

Honor Blackman

Y	F	C	A	T	H	E	R	I	N	E	G	A	L	E
E	A	B	F	H	K	A	J	L	E	N	M	B	V	G
D	D	A	S	B	J	T	E	Y	T	W	H	A	S	G
R	A	T	U	A	R	H	E	Q	B	C	A	J	W	N
U	S	Q	D	F	G	H	I	L	A	G	E	R	Y	I
P	H	A	W	M	V	N	M	E	R	T	O	P	E	K
W	T	S	D	A	V	I	D	K	E	E	L	J	N	A
A	I	C	M	R	K	L	S	D	M	F	C	Z	A	R
X	M	E	Q	T	G	H	J	E	M	K	S	Q	J	A
C	S	A	T	I	V	R	I	S	A	H	N	V	I	T
A	S	C	H	N	Q	T	P	A	P	U	S	E	L	D
V	U	B	A	K	W	Y	O	P	E	T	A	R	O	H
B	N	D	G	I	E	U	L	U	E	B	C	B	K	Y
N	E	V	W	N	Q	A	U	I	L	K	T	R	J	F
K	V	S	Y	G	T	I	B	M	A	G	E	K	I	M

24 EPISODIC TRIVIA – SERIES 3 - PART A

1. **CONCERTO**

   1. Stefan Veliko.   2. A strip club.   3. Russian roulette.   4. Zalenko.
   5. The trade minister.

2. **BRIEF FOR MURDER**

   1. Mrs Catherine Gale.   2. Miles and Jasper Lakin.   3. A fraud and a
   business conspiracy.   4. His bowler hat.   5. On a friend's boat.

3. **THE NUTSHELL**

   1. The 43rd floor.   2. Chocolate.   3. A number code.   4. 95 volts.
   5. Jason.

4. **THE GOLDEN FLEECE**

   1. The Yan Sing restaurant.   2. Mr Lo.   3. Aldershot.   4. In the
   course of duty.   5. £5,000.

21. MANDRAKE

1. Arsenic.   2. St Albans.   3. His former boss.   4. Eye injury.
5. A graveyard.

22. TROJAN HORSE

1. Sebastien II.   2. Caviar and crackers.   3. Scavenger.   4. Major
Pantling.   5. A class in poisons.

23. THE OUTSIDE-IN MAN

1. Mark Charter.   2. Behind a butcher's shop.   3. PANSAC.   4. In
her garter.   5. Shin bones.   6. A tape recorder.

24. THE CHARMERS

1. Cleeves.   2. Martin.   3. In her sewing basket.   4. On holiday in
Morocco.   5. Pimlico.   6. Seek, Hate, Kill.   7. An actress.

25. ESPRIT DE CORPS

1. Three.   2. The Highland Regiment.   3. Bollinger.
4. Queen Anne.   5. He bribed Private Jessop, who was in charge
of the execution squad.

26. LOBSTER QUADRILLE

1. Quentin Slim.   2. In a burned-out hut.   3. A chess piece.
4. Tipped it into the ice bucket.   5. The Bahamas.

27 SERIES 3 – QUICK TEST

1. A) Charles.   2. B) 'The Undertakers'.   3. C) 'November Five'.   4. A)
Lovell.   5. B) The Houses of Parliament.   6. A) Katie.   7. C) Tintin

28 AVENGERS SUDOKU 1

29 UNDER THE HAT 5 - SERIES 3

1. False; director Peter Hammond wanted her to remain tough but Honor Blackman was genuinely overcome.   2. False; but they did star together in the 1964 James Bond movie *Goldfinger*.   3. True.
4. True.   5. True; fade-in style for the first five episodes before the familiar animated style that lasted for the length of series 3.

30 MRS CATHERINE GALE

1. Anthropologist.   2. November Five.   3. 5th October 1930.
4. *'Build A Better Mousetrap'*.   5. *'The Medicine Men'*.   6. Dining and fine wines.   7. Africa.   8. She pretended to be his girlfriend and kissed him.   9. That it's the prelude to a hideous adventure.
10. Primrose Hill, London.

31 EPISODIC TRIVIA – SERIES 4 - PART A

1. **THE MURDER MARKET**

   1. Togetherness.   2. Lead floor to give it weight and hinged sides for an emergency exit.   3. Horse riding.   4. Canada.   5. Jessica Stone.

2. **THE MASTER MINDS**

   1. The Dorrington Dean Academy for Young Ladies.   2. The Arrow; a guided missile.   3. Sixty.   4. To cut the water supply outside the airfield.   5. The cuffs of his shirt.   6. Trampoline.   7. Holly Trent.

3. **DIAL A DEADLY NUMBER**

   1. After two hours.   2. Capillary needle attached to a pager. 3. With a wine cork.   4. 1909 Château Lafite Rothschild.   5. A deadly version of Steed's watch.   6. A bicycle pump gun. 7. Banker.

4. **DEATH AT BARGAIN PRICES**

   1. The basement of the store.   2. Pinters.   3. Thermodynamics. 4. On bicycles.   5. Popple.   6. A washing machine.   7. A black eye.

5. **TOO MANY CHRISTMAS TREES**

   1. Publisher.   2. A brainstorm.   3. A Tale of Two Cities. 4. Freddie Marshall.   5. War Office, Psychiatric Department. 6. 0012.   7. The Hall of Great Expectations.   8. Telepathy. 9. Cathy Gale.   10. Wild Thyme.

6. **THE CYBERNAUTS**

   1. United Automation.   2. He was bulletproof.   3. He died of a broken neck; the other victims had a fractured skull.   4. Two. 5. Radio-controlled pen.   6. Whiplike.   7. Miniature camera. 8. Benson.

7. **THE GRAVEDIGGERS**

   1. Dr Hubert Marlowe.   2. A railway track.   3. Trains.   4. Jamming devices.   5. The Footplate Man's Friendly Society.

8. **ROOM WITHOUT A VIEW**

   1. Three o' clock.   2. Leonard Pasold.   3. Nissan.   4. Seventh floor.
   5. Monsieur Gourmet.

9. **A SURFEIT OF H2O**

   1. Buttercup Brew. 2. Eli.   3. Rain.   4. Steed, Steed, Steed, Steed,
   Steed and Jacques Limited.   5. In a wine press.

10. **TWO'S A CROWD**

    1. Fido. 2. Gordon Webster.   3. PSEV.   4. Crème de violette.
    5. Silver foil.

11. **MAN EATER OF SURREY GREEN**

    1. Miss Sheldon.   2. Professor Taylor, Professor Knight and Dr
    Connelly.   3. Plant diseases.   4. A hearing aid.   5. Emma Peel.

12. **SILENT DUST**

    1. Juggins.   2. A sheriff.   3. Punting on a river.   4. Quince.
    5. Crop Sprayer.

13. **THE TOWN OF NO RETURN**

    1. Little Bazely by the Sea.   2. Marzipan delight.   3. Below.
    4. He burned it with a candle on the bar.   5. The roundabout.

32 AVENGING ACRONYMS

1. Director of Intelligence, Security and Combined Operations.
2. Quite Quite Fantastic. 3. Business Efficiency Bureau. 4. United
Foods and Dressings. 5. Guild Of Noble Nannies. 6. Bi-lateral
Infiltration Great Britain, Europe and North America.
7. Philanthropic Union for the Rescue, Relief and Recuperation of
cats. 8. Permanent Agency for National Security And Counter-
intelligence. 9. Ministry Of Technology – Neoteric Research
Unit. 10. Sociability, Nobility, Omnipotence, Breeding Inc.

33 Episodic Trivia – Series 4 - Part B

14. The Hour That Never Was

1. RAF Hamelin. 2. A rabbit. 3. A milk float. 4. A wedding present. 5. A tree. 6. Eleven o'clock. 7. The milkman.
8. A tramp.

15. Castle De'ath

1. Ian De'Ath. 2. A ghost. 3. The Iron Maiden.
4. ABORCASHAATA; Advisory Bureau On Refurbishing Castles And Stately Homes As A Tourist Attraction. 5. Six inches.
6. The bagpipes.

16. The Thirteenth Hole

1. A .303 rifle. 2. Golf. 3. On a golf course. 4. A porkpie hat.
5. Vostik 2. 6. 11am and 3pm.

17. Small Game For Big Hunters

1. Sherenzi. 2. Cucumber. 3. Tsetse. 4. Great South Road, 23 miles from London. 5. Canoeing.

18. The Girl From Auntie

1. John, Paul, George and Fred. 2. Fancy dress. 3. On a bicycle.
4. Art Incorprated. 5. Ivanoff.

19. Quick-Quick Slow Death

1. A dead body. 2. A rose tattoo. 3. His entire family. 4. Band leader Chester Read. 5. Nicki.

20. The Danger Makers

1. Bacchus. 2. Black. 3. Dr Harold Long. 4. Private Stanhope.
5. The crown jewels.

21. A Touch Of Brimstone

1. Plastic spiders. 2. Drink until the glass is empty. 3. Willie Frant.
4. National Anthem. 5. The Queen of Sin.

22. What The Butler Saw

1. Commander Red, Major White and Squadron Leader Blue.
2. Sgt Moran.   3. He couldn't be bribed.   4. In the officers' uniforms.   5. Ludo.

23. The House That Jack Built

1. A key.   2. Metal spikes.   3. One year.   4. An electronic plunger. 5. Electronic.

24. A Sense Of History

1. St Bodes.   2. Eric Dubuoys.   3. Stone Henge.   4. Robin Hood. 5. Friar Tuck.

25. How To Succeed... At Murder

1. Throgbottom.   2. A toy doll.   3. A ballerina.   4. Leap into My Fervid Arms.   5. Ruination to all men.

26. Honey For The Prince

1. Emma.   2. Cricket.   3. B Bumble.   4. The dance of the six veils. ("She was poorly educated, Your Majesty. Alas, she cannot count.") 5. Chief Eunuch in a harem.

34 Series 4 - Quick Test Part 1

1. B) Brodny.   2. C) V.   3. C) Pongo.   4. B) Toy Aeroplanes.   5. B) Chess Board.   6. A) Ivenko.

35 WORD SEARCH 4 - 'ELLO, STEED; GOT A NEW MOTOR?

A	V	W	A	N	Z	M	B	Y	L	O	B	D	E	E
P	D	F	R	A	N	G	E	R	O	V	E	R	C	P
O	L	S	Y	Q	B	J	B	S	T	N	S	H	K	U
R	I	Y	A	H	Q	A	Q	A	U	F	D	W	L	O
U	O	G	B	K	A	R	E	B	S	R	B	F	N	C
E	J	D	C	E	H	O	O	N	E	A	N	C	M	R
S	H	S	J	L	N	S	K	Q	L	S	J	A	R	A
U	G	T	K	Q	K	T	M	I	A	N	K	B	T	U
T	D	A	L	G	P	E	L	N	N	A	L	D	I	G
O	S	J	Q	A	E	G	M	E	M	C	C	J	K	A
L	B	R	O	L	L	S	R	O	Y	C	E	L	M	J
F	H	K	N	G	D	T	P	G	N	O	W	D	E	K
J	K	W	T	A	W	D	O	D	A	B	C	A	S	A
K	P	Q	U	M	K	A	L	X	S	R	A	T	T	L
S	J	X	R	A	U	G	A	J	P	A	D	M	Z	F

36 SERIES 4 - QUICK TEST PART 2

1. A) Mellors. 2. A) Dr Adams. 3. A) Grindley. 4. B) A dog.
5. B) Laughing gas. 6. A) Torrential rain. 7. C) The heating.

37 BEHIND THE SCENES – SERIES 4

1. C) Laurie Johnson. 2. B) Worker in a pathological morgue.
3. B) 'A Surfeit of H2O'. 4. B) Theatre. 5. A) John Bates.
6. A) 'A Touch of Brimstone'.

38 UNDER THE HAT 5 - SERIES 4

1. True; she played James Bond's wife Tracy in the 1969 Bond film
On Her Majesty's Secret Service. 2. True. 3. True. 4. True. 5. True;
of her 50 episodes the first 26 Diana Rigg shows are in black and
white. 6. True. 7. False; it's a Hunter

39 Episodic Trivia - Series 5 – Part A

1. **The Fear Merchants**
   1. The dark. 2. Wembley Stadium. 3. A quarry. 4. Jeremy Raven.
   5. A lack of champagne. 6. CPC; Central Productivity Council.

2. **Escape In Time**
   1. The Elizabethan Era. 2. Mackidockie Court. 3. She can sew.
   4. Black. 5. Turkeys.

3. **The Bird Who Knew Too Much**
   1. Captain Crusoe. 2. Jordan. 3. To keep it on. 4. Peter J. Elliott.
   5. His umbrella. 6. Top C. 7. Champagne. 8. Heathcliff Hall.
   9. A parrot. 10. An impact grenade.

4. **From Venus With Love**
   1. The British Venusian Society. 2. White. 3. Brigadier Whitehead.
   4. A selection of hats. 5. A laser beam.

5. **The See Through Man**
   1. Quilbie. 2. Elena. 3. With a chop to the hand. 4. A big dog.
   5. File 144.

6. **The Winged Avenger**
   1. Simon Roberts and Son. 2. Eeurrp! 3. Tay Ling. 4. Batman.
   5. Frank Bellamy. 6. Arnie Packer.

7. **The Living Dead**
   1. FOG; Friends of Ghosts. 2. Benedict. 3. Kermit the Hermit.
   4. The cellar. 5. He cut the lift cables.

8. **The Hidden Tiger**
   1. A cat. 2. Like a cat drinking from a bowl. 3. An electrophon.
   4. Major Nesbitt. 5. E to K. 6. A bronze tabby.

9. **The Correct Way To Kill**
   1. SNOB. 2. Olga. 3. A chiropodist. 4. It softens the brain tissues.
   5. Boris Grotski.

10. NEVER, NEVER SAY DIE

1. Professor Frank N. Stone.   2. 20 feet.   3. Two times.   4. Radio.
5. His growth of beard.

11. EPIC

1. Stewart Kirby.   2. Z.Z. Von Schnerk.   3. A film set.   4. MGM.
5. A circular saw.

12. THE SUPERLATIVE SEVEN

1. On a plane.   2. A plastic duck.   3. Gemini.   4. Six.   5. A soldier
from the Duke of Wellington's army.

40 CROSSWORD 3

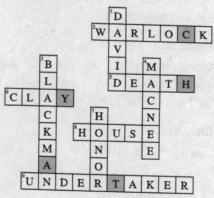

Hidden Name: *Cathy*

41 EPISODIC TRIVIA – SERIES 5 - PART B

13. A FUNNY THING HAPPENED ON THE WAY TO THE STATION

1. The ticket inspector.   2. His umbrella.   3. Train.   4. Husband and
wife.   5. A grateful Prime Minister.

14. SOMETHING NASTY IN THE NURSERY

1. Baby bouncer.   2. General Wilmott.   3. Nanny Roberts.
4. Martins and Son and Son.   5. Lavender.

15. THE JOKER

1. Max Prendergast. 2. Playing cards. 3. Mein Leibling Mein Rose.
4. A house. 5. The dining room. 6. Solitaire.

16. WHO'S WHO???

1. Lola. 2. Red and Blue. 3. Tulip. 4. Philip Levene. 5. Migraine.

17. DEATH'S DOOR

1. A falling chandelier. 2. Sir Andrew Boyd. 3. He was used for
target practice. 4. Brake failure. 5. That she would collide with a
tall dark stranger. 6. Superstitious.

18. RETURN OF THE CYBERNAUTS

1. Brothers. 2. Dr Garnett. 3. A wristwatch. 4. By a cardiograph.
5. Totally, utterly and agonisingly.

19. DEAD MAN'S TREASURE

1. "What a shocking place to find the treasure." 2. Penny Plain.
3. Red. 4. An electric shock. 5. A treasure hunt. 6. At three in
the morning. 7. Two. 8. The reverse setting.

20. THE £50,000 BREAKFAST

1. Borzoi. 2. Charlie. 3. Dusty Rhodes. 4. Miss Pegram.
5. Glover.

21. YOU HAVE JUST BEEN MURDERED

1. Nathaniel Needle. 2. Millionaires. 3. Half Penny. 4. Gilbert
Jarvis. 5. A bomb.

22. MURDERSVILLE

1. Children; Gordon, Julian, Albert and baby Brian. 2. Little
Storping in the Swuff. 3. Dr Haymes. 4. A ducking stool in the
local pond. 5. Three.

23. THE POSITIVE-NEGATIVE MAN

1. His Bentley. 2. 90. 3. Top Hush. 4. Broadcast Power.
5. Risley Dale.

24. MISSION... HIGHLY IMPROBABLE

1. Shaeffer. 2. The Saracen FV603 tank. 3. Dr Chivers.
4. A Rolls Royce. 5. Captain Gifford.

42 MISS TARA KING

1. A brick. 2. 'You'll Catch Your Death'. 3. Tara King's uncle.
4. 'Take Me To Your Leader'. 5. Wigs. 6. A fireman's pole.
7. 9 Primrose Crescent. 8. 69. 9. Her address and phone number.
10. A blonde wig.

43 UNDER THE HAT 7 - SERIES 5

1. True, she was made a Dame in 1994. 2. True. 3. True; the actress
Rachael Stirling. 4. True. 5. False; Joanna Lumley has also
appeared with Eric and Ernie.

44 SERIES 5 - QUICK TEST

1. B) 'The Hidden Tiger'. 2. B) A parrot. 3. B) 'Epic'. 4. A) 'The Fear
Merchants'. 5. B) A plane. 6. C) We're Needed. 7. C) Both.
8. C) The Cybernauts. 9. B) Green. 10. (B) Science.

45 CONUNDRUM 4

Linda Thorson

46 BEHIND THE SCENES – SERIES 5

1. C) Brian Sheriff. 2. A) Gold. 3. A) Rick Wakeman. 4. B) Brian
Clemens & Roger Marshall. 5. B) 'The Strange Case of the Missing
Corpse'. 6. B) Barbara Bain. 7. B) Charles Crichton.

47 EPISODIC TRIVIA – SERIES 6 - PART A

1. THE FORGET-ME-KNOT

1. George Burton. 2. Two weeks. 3. Simon Filson. 4. Two.
5. Giles. 6. A crossword. 7. John Steed. 8. Tea.

2. **INVASION OF THE EARTHMEN**

   1. Alpha Academy.   2. Throwing her opponent through a window.
   3. Boa Constrictor.   4. Places a tissue into it.   5. Green.
   6. Humpty Dumpty.

3. **THE CURIOUS CASE OF THE COUNTLESS CLUES**

   1. Janice Flanders.   2. Skiing.   3. Apples.   4. Snooker.   5. He stands
   on it.   6. Reginald Hubert Dawson.

4. **SPLIT!**

   1. Boris Kartovski.   2. TSI; Top Secret Information.   3. The
   Nullington Private Hospital.   4. Calligraphist.   5. A tall crystal
   glass of crushed ice, permeated with Grenadine, laced with a
   mixture of Cantonese Saki and Creme de Violet, topped with a
   measure of Calvados, a tablespoon of Devonshire cream and a fresh
   unripe strawberry.   6. With his bowler hat.   7. In the heart.
   8. Major Peter Rooke.   9. 1963.   10. Lord Barnes.

5. **GET-A-WAY**

   1. A monastery.   2. Lizard.   3. Smith and Wesson Magnum.
   4. Rostov; turquoise. Lubin; navy blue. Ezdorf; red.   5. Paul Ryder,
   George Neville, John Steed.

6. **HAVE GUNS – WILL HAGGLE**

   1. Colonel Martin Nsonga.   2. FF70.   3. They bounced in on a
   trampoline.   4. Lady Adrianna Beardsley.   5. Sky Blue.

7. **LOOK (STOP ME IF YOU'VE HEARD THIS ONE...)
   BUT THERE WERE THESE TWO FELLERS**

   1. Merry Maxie Martin.   2. An egg.   3. Eat at Joe's.   4. Punch and
   Judy.   5. A vintage-style car horn.   6. Seven.   7. Red-nosed
   comedians.   8. Lemon.

8. **MY WILDEST DREAM**

   1. Dr Jaeger.   2. Lord Teddy Chilcott.   3. Tara King's shoe.
   4. Witnesses.   5. Aggressive therapy.

9. **WHOEVER SHOT POOR GEORGE OBLIQUE STROKE XR40?**

1. Acid. 2. American. 3. She went in as his niece Prunella.
4. An olive. 5. Burned to death. 6. Jason the butler. 7. Tobin.

10. **YOU'LL CATCH YOUR DEATH**

1. The Anastasia Nursing Academy. 2. Grandma. 3. Human
beings and chimpanzees. 4. A straitjacket. 5. Sub Zero.

11. **ALL DONE WITH MIRRORS**

1. In a buttercup field. 2. A swimming pool. 3. Watney.
4. They pushed her clear of the rocks and didn't know she
could swim. 5. A lighthouse. 6. The villains' voices. 7. Light.

12. **SUPER SECRET CYPHER SNATCH**

1. Classy Glass Cleaning. 2. A secretary. 3. The ladder.
4. Roger Jarret. 5. MI12.

13. **GAME**

1. A giant hourglass. 2. Daniel Edmund. 3. Jigsaw. 4. One of
the hands. 5. Steedopoly. 6. Six. 7. Brigadier. 8. Snakes
and Ladders.

14. **FALSE WITNESS**

1. Milk. 2. A double-decker London bus. 3. Melville. 4. Punched
him for lying to him. 5. He had eaten too many oysters.
6. Penman. 7. Dreemy Kreem Dairies. 8. A butter machine.

15. **NOON DOOMSDAY**

1. Department S. 2. Gerald Kafka. 3. Mother. 4. Sunley.
5. In his walking crutch.

16. **LEGACY OF DEATH**

1. A dagger. 2. Fort Steed. 3. A radio-controlled airplane.
4. Sidney Street & Humbert Green. 5. Black.

48 JOHN STEED – PART 1

1. John Wickham Gascoygne Beresford Steed.   2. St James.   3. 5 Westminster Mews.   4. Freckles.   5. Boudles.   6. Aunt Penelope.   7. Whangee Bamboo.   8. Horses.   9. Champagne.   10. 15 ½

49 EPISODIC TRIVIA – SERIES 6 - PART B

17. THEY KEEP KILLING STEED

1. Underground base beneath a quarry.   2. Strawberry shortcake.   3. Six; one shot by Arcos, four created as interference by Steed, and Arcos when he tried to escape.   4. Baron Von Curt.   5. A new submarine.   6. The Royal Navy.   7. Plastic surgery.   8. Baron Von Curt.

18. WISH YOU WERE HERE

1. Charles Merrydale.   2. The hotel kitchen.   3. Basil Creighton-Latimer.   4. Maxwell.   5. SOS.

19. KILLER

1. Lady Diana Forbes-Blakeney.   2. Remote ElectroMatic Agent Killer.   3. Paxton.   4. Dropped from a helicopter.   5. An inflatable dinghy.   6. The Orient.   7. Through the skylight.   8. Napoleon Brandy special reserve.

20. THE ROTTERS

1. A pencil.   2. Her tyres were flat.   3. Inflatable.   4. George & Kenneth.   5. A piano.

21. THE INTERROGATORS

1. TOHE; Test Of Human Endurance.   2. A pigeon.   3. Yogurt.   4. Lt Roy Caspar.   5. Through a telephone box.

22. THE MORNING AFTER

1. A box of luminous dust.   2. 24 hours.   3. Guineas.   4. Brigadier Hansing.   5. A quadruple double agent; the artiste superior of the double-double-double-double cross.

23. LOVE ALL

1. Cricket.   2. Rosemary Z Glade.   3. Perfumers.   4. "You will fall in love with the first person you see."   5. Suicide.

24. TAKE ME TO YOUR LEADER

1. A red briefcase.   2. A dog.   3. Richard Strauss.   4. In the star of her magic wand.   5. A crypt.

25. STAY TUNED

1. On holiday.   2. Father.   3. Collins.   4. Bacchus.   5. Mother.

26. FOG

1. The Gaslight Ghoul.   2. London fog.   3. Edgar Allen Poe. 4. November.   5. A Victorian swordstick.

27. WHO WAS THAT MAN I SAW YOU WITH?

1. The Field Marshal.   2. A boxing ring.   3. Zero minus.   4. 24 hours.   5. Lip reader.   6. She re-enacted how she had been framed with Steed as the target.

28. PANDORA

1. A Rembrandt.   2. Rupert and Henry Lasindall.   3. A French bracket clock.   4. Cathy Gale and Emma Peel.   5. The First World War.

29. THINGUMAJIG

1. Professor Trueman.   2. A black box that delivers high-voltage shocks.   3. Champagne.   4. The organ.   5. Reverend Teddy.

30. HOMICIDE AND OLD LACE

1. Harriet and Georgina.   2. Blonde.   3. Five fingers of Old Red Eye.   4. He wore a bulletproof vest.   5. Intercrime.

31. REQUIEM

1. A cannon.   2. Murder International.   3. She apparently loses the use of her legs.   4. Kisses him on the cheek.   5. His pen.

32. TAKE-OVER

1. Fenton Grenville.   2. Bill and Laura Bassett.   3. February.
4. Invisible golf.   5. By placing a phosper bomb onto his neck.

33. BIZARRE

1. Bagpipes Happychap.   2. In his back yard.   3. Happy Meadows.
4. Helen Pritchard.   5. They were all crooked financiers.

50 AVENGERS SUDOKU 2

51 SERIES 6 - QUICK TEST

1. C) Rhonda.   2. A) A double-decker bus.   3. C) Meudon and
Heim.   4. C) 'Killer'.   5. B) 'Homicide and Old Lace'.   6. B)
Mushroom.   7. B) Unsalted.   8. B) A champagne fountain.

52 JOHN STEED – PART 2

1. Green and red.   2. RKJ de V Steed, his great grandfather.   3. Toy soldiers.   4. Five: Puppy, Freckles, Sheba, Junia and Katie.   5. 3 Stable Mews.   6. Flowers.   7. Four.   8. Anti-clockwise.   9. An umbrella.   10. Bowler Hat.

53 UNDER THE HAT 8 - SERIES 6

1. True.   2. True.   3. True; she appeared on *Star Trek: The Next Generation*.   4. True; he appeared in Roger Moore's seventh and final Bond film *A View To A Kill* in 1985.   5. True.

54 WHO'S WHO??? – PART 1

1. Ronnie Barker.   2. Peter Cushing.   3. Michael Gough.   4. Warren Mitchell.   5. Kate O'Mara.   6. Christopher Lee.   7. Bernard Cribbins.   8. John Cleese.   9. Arthur Lowe.   10. Patrick Mower.

55 JOHN STEED – PART 3

1. 0 to 3.   2. The Adventures of Tintin.   3. Velvet.   4. Chelsea Boots.   5. RAF Hamelin.   6. The swordstick.   7. A diamond tie pin.   8. Horse riding.   9. Steel.   10. John Steed.   11. The George V Hotel.   12. Yes; he is seen diving in *'Castle De'Ath'* and admits over the radio that he can swim in *'Forward Base'*.   13. 21.   14. He calls it his cellar.   15. Three-piece.

56 WHO'S WHO??? – PART 2

1. Penelope Keith.   2. Clive Revill.   3. Patrick Newell.   4. Robert Brown.   5. Geoffrey Palmer.   6. Burt Kwouk.   7. Stuart Damon.   8. Steven Berkoff.   9. Paul Eddington.   10. Julian Glover.

57 Cars

1. Red Jaguar XJS.   2. A Rolls Royce.   3. Three; 1 in the Keel era and 2 in the Tara King era.   4. White.   5. Maroon AC Cobra.
6. Yellow Jaguar XJS.   7. Automatic.   8. Albert Fennell.   9. Bentley.
10. Lotus Europa.   11. Three; a yellow Rover SD1 Automatic, a green Jaguar Coupe and a green Range Rover.   12. A Mini Cooper.

58 Episodic Trivia – The New Avengers – Part A

1. **The Eagle's Nest**

    1. Colonel Bogey.   2. Scotland.   3. Pulling Champagne corks.
    4. Adolf Hitler.   5. A radio in his bowler hat.   6. Smith and Wesson.   7. The Royal Ballet.

2. **The Midas Touch**

    1. Gold.   2. Eating an orange.   3. Hong Kong Harry.   4. A white mouse.   5. Motor racing.

3. **House Of Cards**

    1. Spence.   2. David Miller.   3. Ivan Perov.   4. A capsule in his drink.   5. A special cross sprayed on the roof of his car.   6. Tricky.
    7. The heart.   8. A pork chop.

4. **Last Of The Cybernauts???**

    1. The seducer.   2. Snooker.   3. Mrs Weir.   4. A car park.
    5. Plastic skin.   6. Terry.

5. **To Catch A Rat**

    1. The New Doberman; shortened to the New D.   2. Flyer.
    3. The White Rat.   4. Leipzig.   5. Church.

6. **Cat Amongst The Pigeons**

    1. Zarcardi.   2. Two baskets of cats.   3. A flute.   4. In a swimming pool.   5. Shock.   6. The Sanctuary of Wings.   7. Merton.

7. **TARGET!**

   1. Steed.   2. 100%.   3. 'Steed's hat'.   4. Klokoe.   5. Horse riding.
   6. Three times in a row.   7. Curare.

8. **FACES**

   1. Walton, an Irish alcoholic.   2. Terrison.   3. Base 47.
   4. A pocket watch.   5. Purdey and Gambit.

9. **TALE OF THE BIG WHY**

   1. Bessie's mating habits.   2. Bert Brandon.   3. Shoots them.
   4. Poole and Roach.   5. A roadside burger van.

10. **THREE HANDED GAME**

    1. Cantley.   2. Marshmallows.   3. Memory experts.   4. A stutter.
    5. Racing driver.   6. Tap dancer.   7. He is her nude model.

11. **SLEEPER**

    1. S95.   2. Pyjamas.   3. By coach.   4. His little black book.   5. 19.

12. **GNAWS**

    1. A giant rat.   2. Chislenko.   3. Seismograph activity.
    4. A giant snake and a killer shark.   5. Tomato.

13. **DIRTIER BY THE DOZEN**

    1. 19th Special Commando.   2. Major.   3. In a minefield.
    4. Mad Jack.   5. By helicopter.

59 WHO'S WHO??? – PART 3

1. Garfield Morgan.   2. Pamela Stephenson.   3. Keith Barron.
4. Terence Alexander.   5. Brian Blessed.   6. Charlotte Rampling.
7. Peter Wyngarde.   8. Peter Jeffery.   9. Philip Madoc.
10. John Challis.

60 BEHIND THE SCENES – SERIES 6

1. B) *'All Done With Mirrors'*.   2. B) His ribs.   3. A) *'Have Guns – Will Haggle'*.   4. B) A black dress.   5. A) Leslie Norman.   6. C) *'Split!'*

14. Hostage

1. Simon Oates. 2. Spelman. 3. That he doesn't fight fair. 4. Packer. 5. Suzy. 6. £5,000. 7. A tape recorder containing his instructions.

15. Trap

1. Soo Choy. 2. A broken arm. 3. Marty Brine. 4. George Washington. 5. A horseshoe.

16. Dead Men Are Dangerous

1. A Victorian folly. 2. A stone. 3. Sandy. 4. 1957. 5. It's blown up. 6. "Always leave them laughing."

17. Medium Rare

1. Freddie Mason. 2. Graham Wallace. 3. McBain. 4. Victoria Stanton. 5. The ballet.

18. Angels Of Death

1. In his car. 2. A maze. 3. Coldstream. 4. He loves me/He loves me not. 5. Traction.

19. Obsession

1. His Range Rover. 2. He announced that she was acting under his specific orders. 3. His father. 4. Buckinghamshire. 5. Kilner and Morgan.

20. The Lion And The Unicorn

1. Triple D. 2. The lifts. 3. That he was captured by the very best professionals. 4. France. 5. Boulle. 6. Tangier. 7. Accidentally killed by his own men.

21. K Is For Kill – Part One

1. Toy. 2. Beer is for the thirst and wine is for the senses. 3. His cellar. 4. The letter L. 5. An X5 pin grenade – without the pin!

22. K Is For Kill – Part Two

1. The church bell didn't chime.   2. A cigarette case.   3. A funeral.
4. Stanislav.   5. The Little Mothers of the Earth and Tractor
Drivers and Heavy Industry Award.

23. Complex

1. Scapina.   2. Karavitch.   3. Kent.   4. X41.   5. Water.

24. The Gladiators

1. A working holiday.   2. KGB.   3. Siberia.   4. Tom O'Hara.   5. The
computer stored in the security vault.   6. He added his bowler hat
as a second projectile.

25. Forward Base

1. Agatha.   2. A magnet from a toy fishing game.   3. Bailey.
4. Mark 6 missile guidance circuit.   5. Swans.   6. Ivan Halfhide.

26. Emily

1. The Fox.   2. Palmestry.   3. Steed's bowler hat.   4. Eggs from the
farm.   5. A Bowler and a cowboy hat.   6. The car wash.

62 Quick Test – The New Avengers

1. C) *Fawlty Towers*.   2. A) 'Complex'.   3. C) 'Complex'.   4. A) 'The
Eagle's Nest'.   5. C) George Cowley.   6. C) Red, White and Blue.
7. B) Ballerina.   8. A) June 13th.

63 Who's Who??? – Part 4

1. Anneke Wills.   2. Peter Bowles.   3. Fulton Mackay.   4. William
Franklyn.   5. John Laurie.   6. Nicholas Courtney.   7. Peter Sallis.
8. John Thaw.   9. Iain Anders.   10. Ian Ogilvy.

64 CROSSWORD 4

Hidden Name: *Purdey*

65 CONUNDRUM 4

Joanna Lumley

66 DIAL SOME FRIENDLY NUMBERS

1. 187 episodes.   2. 33 episodes.   3. Tara King.   4. Twice.   5. 20 episodes.   6. 3 times in a row.   7. 55 Years.   8. 6 episodes.   9. Dr David Keel.   10. 3 episodes.

67 STAGE PLAY

1. Leslie Phillips.   2. Simon Oates.   3. Sue Lloyd.   4. Kate O'Mara.   5. A butler.   6. Birmingham Theatre & The Prince of Wales Theatre, London.   7. Terence Feely.   8. Madame Gerda.   9. 'The Superlative Seven'.   10. Unfortunately not; two weeks in Birmingham and three weeks in London.

B	O	N	O	I	T	A	N	R	A	C	B	A	B	H
A	O	Q	A	D	G	S	G	O	B	S	R	F	D	A
D	S	W	Q	A	B	D	A	V	C	L	I	T	T	B
S	V	E	L	E	A	T	H	E	R	W	C	I	E	A
G	J	T	A	E	K	P	I	I	D	U	K	W	U	S
J	E	U	M	B	R	E	L	L	A	I	I	K	D	R
K	T	R	I	F	M	H	T	S	N	P	N	L	G	E
L	L	Y	S	L	B	H	A	K	L	O	H	M	J	L
M	I	I	D	A	X	N	Y	T	M	L	A	A	L	E
C	H	P	P	R	A	B	E	A	N	C	N	N	P	E
N	S	O	A	G	O	K	S	Y	O	S	D	C	U	P
V	F	L	T	O	Q	E	F	P	A	Y	B	O	T	A
I	A	N	T	H	E	S	T	E	R	T	A	N	P	M
C	R	S	E	G	H	T	O	N	M	B	G	P	X	M
N	U	G	R	E	T	R	A	G	S	M	X	J	U	E

69 Location, Location, Location

1. Little Storping in the Swuff. 2. Africa. 3. Elstree. 4. Chelsea.
5. Scotland. 6. Brian Clemens. 7. Aldbury, near Tring.
8. Avengerland. 9. Exmoor. 10. Morocco.

70 Big Finish

1. Edward Woodward. 2. Christopher Benjamin. 3. Julian
Wadham. 4. *The Avengers: The Lost Episodes*, Volume 5. 5. The story
Mother's Day. She played a Russian called Tatiana. 6. Too Many
Targets. 7. Seven. 8. They're father and son. 9. Olivia Poulet.
10. Anthony Howell. 11. Septimus Crump.

71 Under The Hat 9 - The New Avengers

1. True. 2. True. 3. True. 4. True. 5. True. 6. True. 7. True; the
first sequence was used for seven episodes. The familiar lion titles
were used from *'Faces'* onwards.

72 CONUNDRUM 6

Ian Hendry

73 AVENGERS SUDOKU 3

74 THE BIG THINKER

1. The Daleks in *Doctor Who*. 2. 31: *Brought To Book, One For The Mortuary, Brief For Murder, Don't Look Behind You, Build A Better Mousetrap, Dressed To Kill,* The Charmers, *Lobster Quadrille* (with Richard Bates under pseudonym Richard Lucas), *Death At Bargain Prices,* The Town of No Return, A Touch Of Brimstone, What The Butler Saw, The House That Jack Built, How To Succeed... At Murder, Honey For The Prince, The Bird Who Knew Too Much* (from a story by Anthony Marriott), *The Living Dead, The Correct Way To Kill, Epic, The Superlative Seven, A Funny Thing Happened On The Way To The Station* (With Roger Marshall under the pseudonym Brian Sheriff),

The Joker, Murdersville, The Forget-Me-Knot, Split!, They Keep Killing Steed, The Interrogators (with Richard Harris), *The Morning After, Pandora, Requiem, Bizarre.* 3. Howard Blake. 4. *Danger Man; The Girl in the Pink Pyjamas.* 5. Dame Joan Collins. 6. *All Creatures Great and Small.* 7. 'My Word of Honor'. 8. Charlie. 9. Lion.

75 CONUNDRUM 7

Gareth Hunt

76 CROSSWORD 5

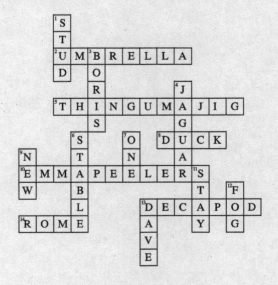

AFTERWORD

The *Avengers* and *The New Avengers* are unique in that they are quintessentially British in the eyes of the world. When they first aired on TV, particularly to overseas audiences, it really shaped how the world viewed Britain and Britishness. We were all fighting diabolical masterminds, had gorgeous London pads and in a matter of moments would be traversing the luscious green countryside in a Bentley, drinking champagne and saving the day. All the women were incredibly agile, sexy, independent and incredibly fashionable and all the men were suave, debonair gentlemen, who wore bowler hats and carried swordstick umbrellas and had a twinkle in their eyes, and all of it served up with a soupçon of surrealism.

I was lucky enough to grow up around one of the main brains behind *The Avengers* and *The New Avengers*, Brian Clemens, who was my father. Over the years, my parents hosted many dinner parties which would see many creatives from in front of and behind the camera who made these shows come to life, and one thing that I noticed which was a common theme that they all experienced: laughter. Everyone on *The Avengers* seemed to have a fantastic time making the shows and only spoke incredibly fondly of their memories, recounting the hilarity of a moment, getting that shot, an anecdote when something went awry or simply what an honour it was to be a part of it. Everyone loved working on it and wanted to be a part of it.

Directing the audio drama comic strip versions of *The Avengers* for Big Finish Productions has given me an even clearer insight into the show and the fans. It reminds me of *Doctor Who*, in that each generation has 'their' Doctor. If someone is a fan of the show, they have their favourite 'Avenger girl', from the game-changing Honor Blackman, to the legacy-defining Diana Rigg, to the bewitching bombshell Linda Thorson and the truly, incomparably charming Joanna Lumley, not forgetting of course the first Avenger, the suave and precise Ian Hendry and the last, the jocularly sophisticated Gareth Hunt. All of them were magnificently supported by the inimitable and desperately charismatic Patrick Macnee, without whom, who as my father used to say, the show would not have worked. 'Patrick was *The Avengers*' he would always say. So, like everyone who has their 'Doctor', fans of the show have their 'Avenger' and I am continually meeting new fans, who are discovering it on re-runs or on streaming or DVD and Blu-Ray to great delight.

I think it survives for a number of reasons. One, because the show was incredibly well made and, from the Diana Rigg era and onwards, shot on

35mm film. Two, it starred some of the finest actors of the day and was made by some of cinema's greatest craftsmen and women, and three, there is nothing else like it.

The Avengers lives on in the subconscious. The iconography of the English gentleman with the bowler hat and brolly and the woman in the leather cat suit are burnt into our collective consciousness, whether we know it or not. It has been admired and parodied, and creatives still continue to draw inspiration from it. Mulder and Scully's relationship in *The X-Files* was inspired by Steed and Mrs Peel, Austin Powers took comedic inspiration from the show, along with the Bond franchise and, more recently, *The Kingsman* films; while Colin Firth's Harry Hart is almost a re-incarnation of John Steed. Despite all the tipping of the bowler to all these series and films, it very much lives in a fantasy version of the UK in the swinging 60's and 70's, and is very difficult to transpose to another time. It is a beautiful, witty, classy, thrilling and charming time capsule of a multiverse we would all love to live in, and aren't we lucky that we can.

Sam Clemens
September 2023

PICTURE ACKNOWLEDGEMENTS

Mrs Emma Peel / Conundrum 1 / Series 1 Part A / Series 1 Quick Test / Series 1 Behind The Scenes / Series 2 Quick Test / Series 2 Quick Test 2 / Series 2 Behind The Scenes / Series 3 Part A / Series 3 Part B (Pgs 64 & 69) / Mrs Catherine Gale / Series 4 Part A / Series 4 Part B / 'Ello Steed, Got A New Motor?' / Series 4 Quick Test 2 / Series 4 Behind The Scenes / Series 5 Part A (Pg 97) / Series 5 Part B (Pg 101) / Series 6 Part A (Pg 115) / Series 6 Part B (Pg 126) / Series 6 Quick Test / Crossword 4 / Clothes Maketh The Avenger / Conundrum 6 / The Big Thinker / Congratulations Letter

Images licensed by Studiocanal.

Crossword 1 / Conundrum 2 / Dr David Keel / Have A Word! / Crossword 2 / Series 2 Part A / Series 2 Part B (Pg 50) / Conundrum 3 / Partners / Series 3 Part B (Pg 66) / Series 5 Part A (Pgs 95 & 98) / Series 5 Part B (Pg 103) / Conundrum 4 / Series 6 Part A (Pg 118) / Series 6 Part B (Pg 128) / Conundrum 5 / Dial Some Friendly Numbers / Avengers Sudoku / Conundrum 7

Screen captures/image captures used by kind permission of Studiocanal.

Series 2 Part B (Pg 48)

Sourced from Ian Davey and used by kind permission of Studiocanal.

Series 4 Part A (Pg 79) / Avenging Acronyms / Series 4 Quick Test 1 / Miss Tara King / John Steed Part 1 & 3 / Who's Who Parts 1–4 / Cars / The New Avengers Part A (Pgs 144 & 146) / The New Avengers Part B (Pg 156)

Original artwork courtesy of Brett Jones.

Crossword 3

Sourced from dailymail.co.uk and used by kind permission of Studiocanal.

Series 5 Quick Test

Sourced from guardian.com and used by kind permission of Studiocanal.

John Steed Part 2

Illustration courtesy of Andrew Parsons

The New Avengers Part B (Pg 153)

Image courtesy of Alamy

The New Avengers Quick Test

Original artwork courtesy of Pete Wallbank.

Stage Play

Poster image courtesy of Andrew Stocker.

Location, Location, Location

Photographs supplied by Roy Bettridge.

Big Finish

Cast photographs (Pg 167 & 168) courtesy of Big Finish Productions.

The Avengers: The Lost Episodes Volume 1 & The Avengers: Too Many Targets – designed by Anthony Lamb

The Avengers: The Comic Strip Adaptations Volume 7 – designed by Rafe Wallbank.

Crossword 5

Screen capture from opening titles to The New Avengers episode; The Last of The Cybernauts...??

In Memoriam

Paul O'Grady; images courtesy of Shutterstock and Big Finish Productions

Laurie Johnson; screen captures and images used with kind permission of Studiocanal. The Professionals image reproduced by kind permission of ITV Studios Ltd.

Ray Austin; Screen captures and images used by kind permission of Studiocanal.

Foreword

Image courtesy of Dame Joanna Lumley

Score Sheet

Top Secret stamp used under Free License from Vecteezy.com

Under The Hat 1 – 9

Images courtesy of Sarah Sorkin at Propstore.com

Afterword

Image courtesy of Sam Clemens

The Author

Image courtesy of Brett Jones

All images within this book have been assessed and approved by Studiocanal.

ACKNOWLEDGEMENTS

This book has been a dream come true to write and so many have shared the adventure along the way. My thanks go to:

Neil Griffin, Scott Edwards, Helen Craven, Robert Wheatley, Matthew Lynch, Curtis Quincey, Shaquille Bartley, Aaron Marr, Craig Warwick, Tracey MacInness, Alan Lambert, Sharon Wilkinson, Lilian Start, Erik Hakobyan, Ali York, Kathryn Burton, Ivetka Kosova, Ana Vaduva, Adina Iordache, Millie Beattie, Zoe Beattie, Poppy Beattie, Lottie Beattie, Tanya Fraser, Danielle Guild, Mia Guild, Danielle Pizzimenti and all my friends and colleagues at Newlands (past and present) for their continued support.

Thanks to Dave Rogers; your belief and counsel in this project was unfaltering. To Brett Jones; your tireless support and contributions make this book extra special for me. To my fellow Avengers kin: Mark Witherspoon, Andrew Stocker, Des Glass, Andrew Parsons, Alan & Alys Hayes, Anthony Berryman – I love you all and thank you for your encouragement for this project from its inception.

Special thanks to Pete Wallbank for sharing his time and his work. To Ian Davey and Cyd Child for question verification in certain sections.

Special thanks to Matthew Lynch for giving Sudoku an Avengers twist especially for this project.

Special thanks to Duncan Lilly and Damien May for their help and assistance. Proofreading by Liz Sourbut.

Special thanks also to Nathan & Susan Grooby, Ash Walker, Craig Chapman, Laura Martin, Barry Musgrave, Rebbecca & Kayleigh Heath-O'Brien, Kirstie Lunness-Gardner, Natalie Lunness-Gardner, Peter Lunness, Sandie Lunness, Toni Lunness, Ryan Lunness, Liam Creighton and Niall Creighton – my love to you all.

To the many who have followed me on my journey with The Avengers from the moment it entered my life; you all know who you are and I thank you for sticking by me.

Thank you to my biggest supporters: my late grandmother Rita, my late mother Iris, my late father Roy Senior, my late uncle Luke – I love and miss you all. My brother Martin; I'm nothing without your support. To Emma, Louis, Robert and Hannah; I love you all. To Laura, I thank you for your patience on yet another Avengers project. To Oliver; you make me proud every day – I'm the luckiest father in the world to have you as a son.

Extra special thanks to Massimo Moretti at Studiocanal.

To Quoit Media for your support and belief in this project from the first suggestion.

To the team at Big Finish Productions for their time, help and support.

A very special message to Dame Joanna Lumley and Sam Clemens; thank you both for making a dream come true and devoting your valuable time to this project.

THE AUTHOR

Roy Bettridge has been writing since the age of 15 and has been a fan of *The Avengers* for nearly thirty years.

He has independently published seven titles, beginning with his debut novel: *Look (Stop Me If You've Heard This One...) But There Was This TV Show*, published in 2016. He has also been involved with two Avengers-based charity projects; he contributed to the *Avengerworld* anthology (edited by Alan Hayes) and to *Stay Tuned to The Avengers* Volumes 1 and 2 by Dave Rogers.

Alongside his *Avengers*-related work, he has also released a standalone novel, *Flood*, via 3P Publishing; with more titles to come.

He currently resides in Kettering, Northamptonshire, with his family.